A NOSTALGIC BOARD GAME FOR TWO PLAYERS

War · II

...ND EXCITEMENT ...AT WAR

...n enemy U-boat hit home. Yes, **HOLD** ...**GHT** as you prepare to parachute ...nto occupied Europe as the fight-back ...egins.

...ut its not all blood and guts. ...emember the good times? The sing-...longs around the piano in crowded ...omb shelters. Dame Vera Lynn ...aising our hearts with her nightingale ...oice. And those fleeting wartime ...omances with gallant soldiers home ...n leave. Yes, they were happy times ...s well as sad. And now you can relive ...hem all in this exciting, action-packed ...oard game.

RATIONING

..."Yes, we have no bananas", say ...hopkeepers around Britain as ...ation books come into use. ...ausages, eggs, sugar – even ...rousers are rationed. But good ...ld British spunk is as abundant ...s ever, and beleaguered Britain ...eeps smiling through.

D-DAY

At last Britain bounces back! An armada of small boats, private yachts, ferries, fishing boats and rubber dinghies set sail for Dunkirk. On board thousands of British troops eager to have a crack at the krauts. Within days Berlin has fallen.

THE GOOD OLD DAYS ARE HERE AGAIN

THE GERMAN SURRENDER

Hitler throws in the towel, and Germany surrenders, promising that they won't do it again. At last the British troops can return home, victorious, to their families and friends. Except the ones who've been killed.

WE'VE WON THE WAR

SCAPPA FLOW

In the most fierce sea battle of the entire war the British Navy corner and sink half the German fleet, including the battleships Bismark, Turpitz and Belgrano. Once again Britannia rules the waves.

10 **11** **9** **12** **8** **7** **FINISH**

THE BATTLE OF BRITAIN

The skies above England are filled with the sound of fierce 'dog fighting' as a handful of gutsy British Spitfire pilots, out-numbered ten to one by their evil Nazi counterparts, make short work of the German Luftwaffe.

VICTORY

We won the war again, but just to be sure America drops an atom bomb on Hiroshima.

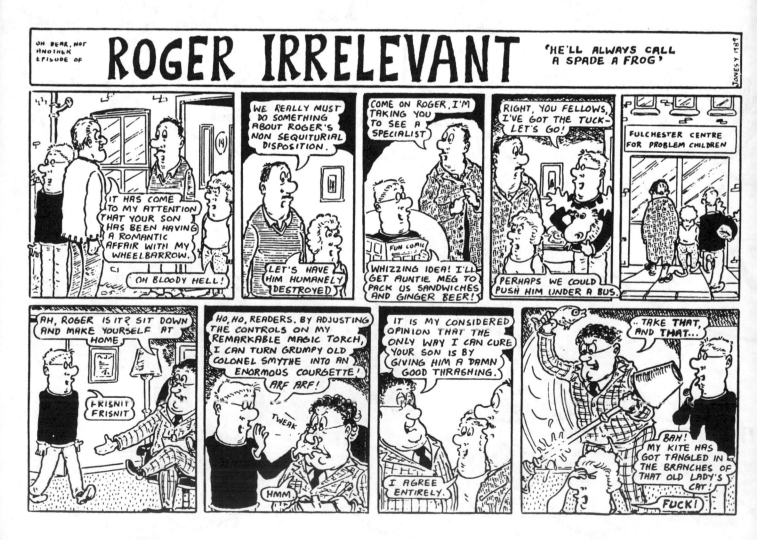

ROGER IRRELEVANT

VIZ
THE SAUSAGE SANDWICH

Stuffed with the porkiest pages from issues 38 to 42

Written, drawn and produced by
CHRIS DONALD
GRAHAM DURY, SIMON THORP
and SIMON DONALD

With contributions by
DAVEY JONES, GRAHAM MURDOCH
RAY FURY
MARTIN LANGSTON, T. BAM
Photography by Colin Davison

ISBN 1 870 870 23 9

Published in Great Britain by John Brown Publishing Limited
The Boathouse, Crabtree Lane, Fulham, London SW6 8NJ
First printing, September 1991

I thought my slipper was a beetle!

I was enjoying a nice cup of tea in my front room when I suddenly caught sight of what I thought was a large beetle out of the corner of my eye. Luckily it was just my slipper that I had kicked off the night before.

N. Blackett-Ord
Ashton-under-Lyme

I don't accept all this nonsense that's talked about enamel buckets. I am 52 and can strongly recommend them. When I was carrying my son, Jason, I always used an enamel bucket and now he's a strapping six-footer.

Mrs. Paula Mills
Coventry

Three cheers for the train drivers!

I think train drivers deserve a large pay rise. The skill required in their job is vastly under-rated. How they steer long trains around bends and manage to keep them on those thin rails is a miracle. Tube drivers deserve even more as they do it in the dark.

Ian Allden
Leeds

"The train arriving on platform 4 is the 18.35 to Staines" said the announcer at my local railway station. Expecting the train to arrive ON the platform I jumped for the safety of the track, whereupon I was hit squarely by an Intercity 125. When are British Rail going to get it right and give their fare-paying passengers accurate information.

D. Silcock
Bracknell

If scientists positioned a large concave mirror in orbit around the earth, the sun's rays would fall on Britain during the night as well as the day, and we could become the world's leading tomato growers.

Dr. Granville Canty
Hebden Bridge

I agree with S. Jones (last issue) that consumer terrorism has gone too far. Yesterday I dropped a jar of strawberry jam on the kitchen floor. Luckily for me it broke because as I was clearing it up, I found hundreds of fragments of broken glass hidden in the jam. I shudder to think what could have happened had I not dropped it.

A. Guindi
Lee Green

Last week I bouht a £750 telescope to watch the recent lunar eclipse. The appointed time came and went but the moon did not seem to eclipse. Imagine my disappointment when I realised I'd been watching a street lamp 30 miles away.

P. Turton
Leeds

999/'99' Mix-Up

I was hit and seriously injured by a speeding car on a zebra crossing recently, while out shopping with my 3-year-old daughter. She seemed quite unimpressed by all the commotion and sat happily playing with her toys while a passerby called for an ambulance. When it eventually arrived her eyes lit up. "Mammy, can I have a 99?", she asked. The poor darling had mistaken the ambulance for an ice-cream van.

Mrs. V. Liar
Redding

Why provide free parking spaces in towns for people who carry a "disabled" parking badge. If I paid 50p to park in a car-park and then developed a headache, I wouldn't expect to get my money back. The trouble with these people is that they want everything for nothing.

Mr. W. Herringbone
Falmouth

What's all this fuss about free eye tests. The only people who object to paying for check-ups are the so-called do-gooders, most of whom wear glasses already. Why should I, and others like me, who have perfectly good eyesight pay higher taxes to subsidise treatment for the blind?

Mr. G. Brown
Berking

I clean my teeth

I am 82 years of age and have never once gone to bed without brushing my teeth thoroughly, even during the war. Can any other readers better this?

Mrs. Patricia Hamilton
Bury St. Edmonds

Well, can you? Are you and old person who has stuck rigidly to a routine involving personal hygiene? Perhaps you have cut your toenails at the same time each week, or cleaned the wax out of your ears with monotonous regularity. Write and let us know. Send your letters to our letterbox address and mark them "Geriatric Hygiene Habits".

My husband had always dreamt of being a professional footballer. But after serving in the merchant navy during the war and then on the railways, he ended up working in insurance until his recent retirement. But now, at 68, he has taken up football again. He has been in training for over a month, and has written to several clubs asking for a trial.

It only goes to show – you're never too old to change your career.

Mrs. E. Brookes
Brinkley

Holiday friendship continues

During a recent holiday at a cottage in the countryside my 4-year-old son made a rather unusual friend – a cow that lived in a field nearby. When our holiday was over he was heartbroken at having to part with his new pal. He was still in tears hours later after our long journey home.

You should have seen his face light up when I led him out into our back garden. My husband had somehow managed to get the cow into the back of our car and had found it a new home – in our coal-shed. Needless to say our son is delighted.

Mrs. E. Redmund
Swansea

Prison Governors who claim their prisons are overcrowded should face the 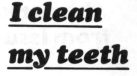 war ... nes. 200 ... live, eat and sl... on a ... ine no bigge ... ecker bu... t com... pla... ...hes... re su... ...osed to ... g prison – not 4-star hotels.

Able Seaman D. McGough
(Retired)
Cumbernauld

Do you think our prisons are over-crowded? Are the inmates getting a raw deal, or do they deserve everything they get? Perhaps you're in prison. If so, write and tell us how much room you've got. Enclose a sketch if necessary. Send your letters to our usual address and mark the envelopes "How much room we've got in prison".

While out playing football recently my 68-year-old husband suffered a heart attack and died.

Let this be a warning to other elderly folk. Too much exercise, especially in later life, can be a dangerous thing.

Mrs. E. Brookes
Brinkley

ᴛᴏᴘ ᴛɪᴘs

BY joining together dozens of paper clips you can make yourself an attractive chain mail tank-top. Ideal for a 'knight' out.

Paul Harvey
Ash Green

BY simply fixing a mirror to your ceiling you can examine your feet without looking down.

L. C. Anderson
Paris

SAVE time when playing darts by attaching a length of string to each dart. After throwing, a sharp tug on the string will return the darts to you.

Patrick Matthews
Bolton

HELP blind people in the post office by licking their stamps for them, or teach their dogs to do so.

Mr. Beakey
Byker

HELP the local police by popping into the mortuary each day to see if you can identify any of the bodies.

J. Lewis
Lichfield

ᴸᴵᴰᴬ
you're late
the sun." y phon.
airport em ere's
a bomb . ne.
on't for
ht nnn.
and
rdicnest

USING string, nails and pullies, it is possible to turn on the taps in the bathroom from your living room.

E. Barnpot
Devon

KEEP a hammer by the bed in case any nails fall out of the ceiling at night.

Nick Dwyer
Brighton

FILL a Shredded Wheat with pink soap and hey presto – an inexpensive brillo pad.

Mrs. B. Parkinson
Harrow

SAVE buying Viz each month by simply changing the colour of the last issue's cover using a wax crayon. Then simply re-read the same old jokes.

M. Reynaud (Mrs.)
Surrey

THAT'S MAGIC!

A Rotherham man claims he was hypnotised and forced to a commit a series of crimes by leading TV magician Paul Daniels.

And Albert Thompson, 37, claims that he has been wrongfully **IMPRISONED** as a result of Daniels' TV Trickery. As well as his freedom, Thompson claims that 'not a lot' star Daniels has cost him his livelihood and now his marriage. For Albert's wife Marjory has walked out on her troubled husband.

"I'm ruined", he told us from the prison cell that has become his home. "What did I ever do to Paul Daniels to deserve this?"

ENTRANCED

Albert's problems began several months ago when he was sitting with his wife watching Daniels' popular TV magic show. "As I watched Daniels perform a hypnotism act I became entranced. I couldn't move. Suddenly I was under his power."

HYPNOTIC

Albert believes that chirpy five footer Daniels had deliberately entangled him in a hypnotic web from which there was no escape. "Apart from a few minor assaults and burglaries, I'd never been in trouble before. But the next thing I knew I'd gone down to the pub, had a few pints and become involved in a fight. It was totally unlike me – completely out of character."

SUBCONSCIOUSLY

Albert blames the fracas on hypnotic messages relayed to him subconsciously by the TV trickster. "The next morning I awoke in a police cell, with a terrible headache, and was charged with assaulting a police officer. I tried to explain to them what had happened but they didn't want to know."

THEFT

Later that day when officers visited Albert's home they discovered several hundred yards of stolen copper cable hidden under blankets in the garage. "I immediately realised this was another of Daniels' conjuring tricks, but my pleas fell on deaf ears. I was charged with theft, and remanded on bail for a fortnight."

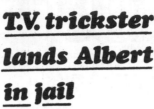

T.V. trickster lands Albert in jail

Albert spent the next two weeks hoping and praying that the hypnotic spell had worn off. But his nightmare was far from over. Soon afterwards he was sacked from his job as lavatory attendant at the local bus station after a large number of toilet rolls were found in his van. "How they got there only Paul Daniels knows", said Albert. "But I had no evidence to link him with all these crimes. He'd set me up good and proper."

PUPPET

A few days later Albert's wife walked out claiming he had assaulted her. "I have no recollection of that at all," he told us. "My mind blacks out completely, and I become a puppet under Daniels complete control. I tried explaining this to my wife, but she said I was drunk and has refused to speak to me."

KITCHEN

Worse was to come. Albert decided to phone Daniels and plead with him to break his spell, but he didn't have any change for the phone box. "I went into the post office to ask for a ten pence piece, and that was all I can remember. When I awoke I was sitting in the kitchen of my council flat counting

money. Suddenly the police broke in – and accused me of robbing the post office. I was completely stunned. I don't know where all the money came from. It was obviously just another one of Daniels' tricks."

LOUNGE

Albert told police that a shotgun found in his bedroom, allegedly used in the robbery, was also conjured up by the TV illusionist. "I may as well have been talking to myself. They simply bundled me into a van and later that evening I was charged with armed robbery."

Several letters written to the top magician and game show host begging him to appear in court to clear Albert's name remain unanswered. "My only hope of justice is that Daniels will own up. But I've heard nothing from him."

CONSERVATORY

Albert is currently being held on remand, pending psychiatric reports. But his hopes of an early release look slim. Meanwhile the Home Office remain tight-lipped over the allegations that Albert is an innocent victim of a TV hypnotist's private joke. "We have no comment to make," they told us yesterday.

'Not a lot' TV Star Daniels.

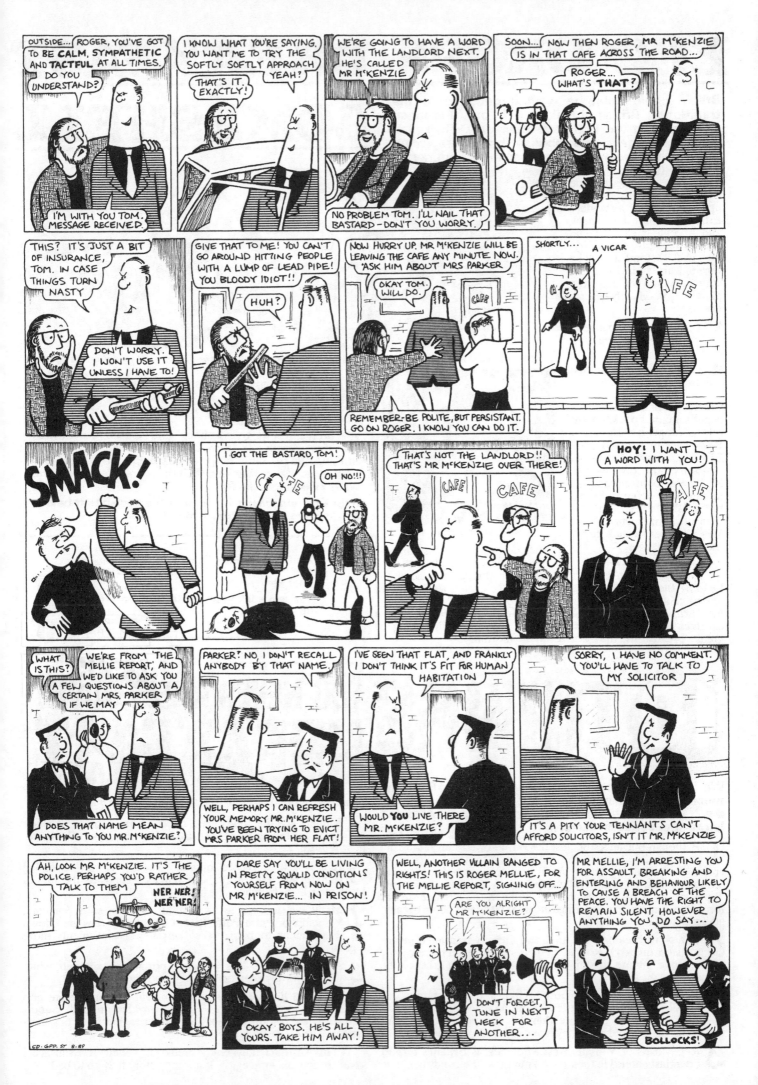

9

EEC DROPS BREAKFAST

BOMBSHELL

Britain could soon be waving goodbye to the traditional British breakfast if our European colleagues in the EEC have their way. They plan to ban bangers and abolish bacon, replacing them with scrawny, unappealing 'continental breakfasts'.

Common Market food chiefs are already drawing up their plans for a standard European morning meal, and it could mean the end for our favourite British fry-ups. In 1992 stomachs will be turning up and down the country as we wake up to a plateful of ghastly Euro-nosh.

OUT will go bangers, bacon, fried egg, tea and toast.

IN will be coffee, croissants, onions and French bread.

Chancellor of the Exchequer Nigel Lawson hopes to fight off European Breakfast Proposals at a meeting of EEC breakfast bosses in Brussels later this month. He'll have to do some tough talking to defend British breakfast tables, and is under firm instructions from Mrs Thatcher to stick up for the British banger.

GREASY

Leading the campaign for a united European morning meal are the French. As well as thick black coffee and greasy bread rolls, they will

The traditional British breakfast (left) could soon be replaced by the scrawny continental version on the right.

Mr. Lawson yesterday.

include garlic, snails and frog's legs on their international breakfast menu. But the scheme is also being opposed by the Belgians. They insist on stuffing themselves with cakes first thing in the morning.

JOIN IN THE FIGHT

We aren't going to sit back and watch our British breakfast disappear from breakfast tables throughout Britain. We're launching a campaign to Save Our Sausages. We're backing Britain's breakfast, and we want **YOU** to join the fight.

Help save our bacon by signing the declaration below, and sending it to the President of France.

To: The President of France, Paris, Europe.

Dear Sir
You can stick your 'continental breakfast' up your arse.

Signed _____

10 THINGS YOU NEVER KNEW ABOUT BREAKFAST

We all love a good old British breakfast. But how much do we really know about our first meal of the day? Tuck into these ten things you probably didn't know about your breakfast ...

1 Although our ancestors lost the Battle of Hastings, they did manage to destory the invading Normans' supply of croissants by setting them on fire, a scene which, as every schoolboy knows, was vividly depicted in the famous Bayeux Tapestry. After his victory in 1066, William the Conqueror was forced to sample the full English breakfast, and soon became addicted to bacon and eggs!

2 The word breakfast is Latin, and literally translated means to 'stop quickly'. Roman soldiers on the march were only allowed one minute to stop for their morning meal, hence the name.

3 Kelloggs, Britain's foremost breakfast manufacturers, are famous for the '57 varieties' of breakfast cereal. Nowadays they manufacture many more than 57 varieties, and some of them, such as Corn Flakes, they make especially for the Queen.

4 Reg Morris of Walsall, West Midlands, is Britain's biggest breakfast eater. He took only 3 minutes 10 seconds to eat 96 sausages for breakfast one morning in December 1986.

5 Kippers – a flat, bony kind of fish – are another of Reg's breakfast favourites. He scoffed 27 in just under 17 minutes in May 1988.

6 Reg is also a record breaker when it comes to eating frankfurters. He finished off 30 in 64 seconds on the 10th of December 1986. However, he had these for dinner.

7 Many old folk prefer a plateful of prunes to porridge, Weetabix or Puffa Puffa Rice. Gluttonous grans gulp down the dried plums to help make their bowel movements more regular.

8 A 'Breakfast TV' is a small, portable black and white television which can be viewed in the kitchen.

9 Breakfast has been the key ingredient in many recent pop successes, among them UB40's 'Breakfast In Bed', Supertramp's 'Breakfast In America', and countless hits by sixties chart toppers The Marmalade.

10 In Australia they enjoy breakfast – kangaroo sausages, bacon and emu eggs – last thing before they go to bed!

SHIT THICK!

Shame of D.J.'s who cannot spell their names

Many of Radio One's top disc jockeys are so stupid they are unable to spell their own names. And at least one of the highly paid 'jocks' is TOTALLY ILLITERATE.

These are the shock claims being made by Randy Blenkinsop, 38, who has been a disc jockey himself for over twenty years.

PLANK

"Many of the so-called 'top names' on Radio One are as thick as short planks," Randy told us, speaking from the garden shed which has become home to his booming disco hire operation. "In fact I heard from a very good source that only one daytime DJ in the current Radio One line up has any academic qualifications at all – a solitary CSE in domestic science."

SIMPLE

Randy claims that even the simplest links between records have to be scripted and rehearsed over and over again before the simple jocks can get them right. "One popular DJ had to be sent to night classes before he took over the Top Forty Show. He was unable to read the chart countdown, and had never counted up to forty before."

DAFT

"Every single show is recorded weeks in advance, and it often takes them 10 or 12 hours just to record a simple 3 hour show."

Randy denies that there is any element of sour grapes in his accusations, but admits that he has been refused auditions for Radio One on several occasions. "I've sent them tapes before, but they didn't even bother replying. One of the reasons is probably that I'm tall and fairly good looking. It's a well-known fact in the business that most of the Radio One guys are less than 5 feet tall, and alongside me they'd look a bit daft."

Indeed Randy claims that BBC boffins use special effects to make their DJs appear normal when they appear on TV. "When they do Top Of The Pops you never see their feet. That's because they always stand on boxes. And they always get loads of people to stand around them. That's so you can't see how fat they are." Randy claims that one DJ stands a mere 4 feet 6 inches tall, and weighs in at almost 18 stone. "He has to spend 10 hours in make-up before they allow him on Top Of The Pops. If you met him in the street you'd run a mile," said Randy.

Randy has no regrets having missed out on a Radio One career. "It's their loss, not mine," he insists. "In fact, if they offered me a job tomorrow, I'd probably turn it down. And in any case I'm fully booked doing Christmas discos most weekends from now until January,"

Top Radio One DJ 'Diddy' David Hamilton. We have no evidence to suggest that he is unintelligent. However he is quite short.

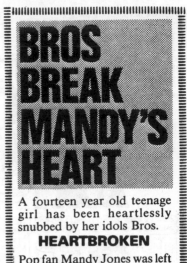

INTENSIVE COMA WARD.

WHY DON'T YOU COME ROUND FOR A COFFEE SOME TIME?

11

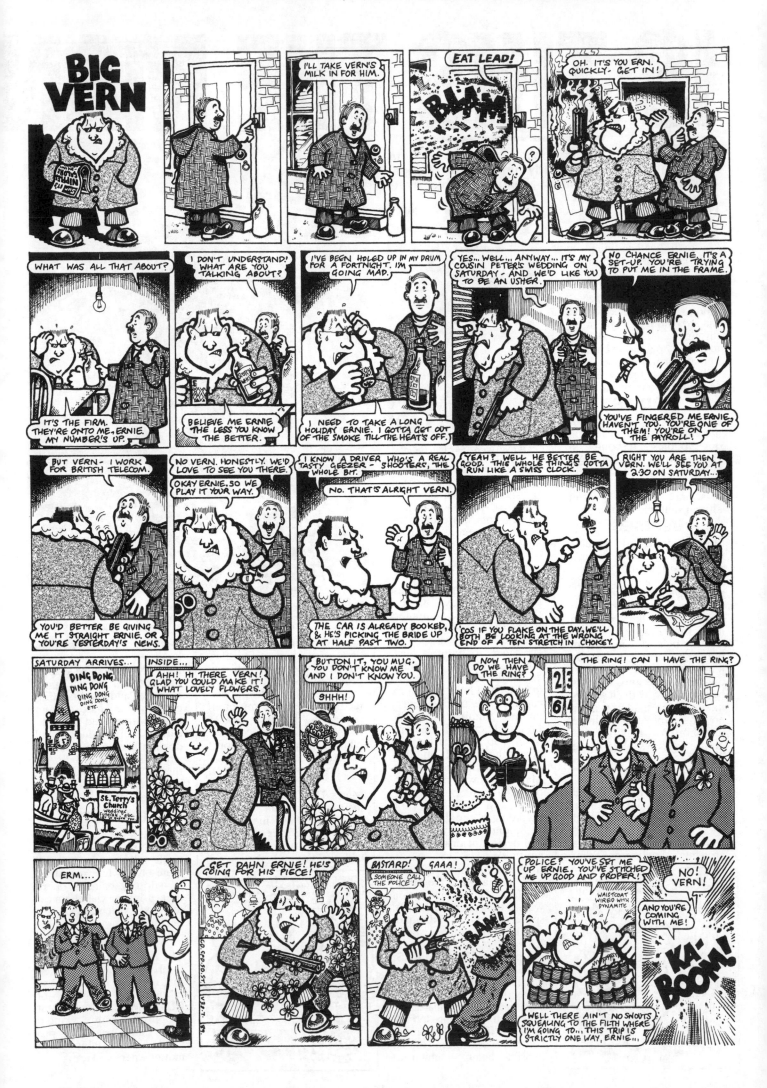

IS THIS THE MAN

Over millions of years, since the dawn of time began, man has constantly undergone change, adapting to meet the challenges of his ever-changing environment.

From the moment millions of years ago when fish-like men first crawled out of the sea man has continued to undergo a series of dramatic evolutionary changes that have altered our physical appearance beyond recognition. From small lobster shaped aquatic creatures, through four legged monkey, ape and eventually human form, man has come full circle on the evolutionary roundabout of change.

BODIES

So what future lies ahead for the human race? How will our bodies respond to changes in the environment? What will man look like in the year 2000? With the help of science, perhaps we can answer that question.

BERRIES

Study of prehistoric remains show clearly that man's **ARMS** are getting shorter. There was a time many years ago when prehistoric man picked berries from tall trees, and walked with his long arms dragging on the ground behind him. Today our arms aren't nearly as long, fitting comfortably into our trouser pockets. Experts believe that with less demands being made on arms nowadays they will continue to shorten, making our obsolete elbows things of the past.

BUSIER

Unlike our arms, **HANDS** have become busier. Man has entered the computer age, and our ten fingers work flat out to operate the growing keyboards that

A man as we see him today.

larger computers demand. The fingers of the future will be shorter – perhaps with only one joint – but there will be lots more of them. Perhaps as many as ten on each hand.

BRAINS

Our **HEAD** is the heaviest part of our body. But like the cumbersome computers of the fifties and sixties, our bulky **BRAINS** will soon be consigned to nature's dustbin. Instead man will think **10 MILLION** times as quickly, and have a memory capable of storing every phone number in the London telephone directory. Microscopic brains the size of a pinhead will be nature's answer to the micro chip. Man's head will, as a result, be much smaller – about the size of a golf ball, and according to the experts will be mounted on a long, flexible neck, not disimilar to a giraffe's.

In the future man will look back and laugh at the primitive forms of communication we use today. Old fashioned speech will be as redundant as the cave man's spear. Instead we will have developed **RADAR EARS**, looking more like satellite dishes than the ears we see today. And our poor eyesight will be unheard of. Man will be using **INFRA RED VISION**. 'Remote control' eyes will send out an invisible beam – similar to

Commuting to work will only take seconds – an artists impression of man in the year 2000.

the TV controls we use today – and high quality 'flat screen' TV pictures will be produced inside your head, complete with Ceefax. Spectacles will become museum pieces in the year 2000. If your vision becomes blurred, simply change your batteries!

BISCUITS

Man's **TEETH** have become increasingly small through the ages. The 7 inch razor sharp teeth of our cave man ancestors disappeared along with the dinosaurs they were

used for eating. As man's diet has evolved, so have his teeth. Now we have smaller, flat teeth for chewing potatoes, rice and biscuits. More convenience foods, combined with a need for faster eating, will produce small, dolphin-like teeth, inside a streamlined, 'duck' bill. And there'll be a pelican style pouch for storing food for short periods.

BREASTS

Bad news for dentists in the year 2000. 'Self drilling' teeth will automatically fill themselves while you sleep, in a totally painless operation, using special chemicals secreted by dental glands in the mouth.

BOTTOMS

The digestive system of the future will be so efficient that man will have no waste products to dispose of. **BOTTOMS** will be for seating purposes only – a kind of flesh filled 'beanbag', providing a comfortable seat no matter where you are.

OUCH!

RIGHT MATE! YOU'RE NICKED!

...THEN I DID THE THREE PEAKS AND THE PENNINE WAY AND THEN I DID THE LYKE WAKE WALK AND AFTER THAT I DID THE...

TAKE NO NOTICE OF MY WIFE. SHE TENDS TO RAMBLE.

OF THE FUTURE?

Many people today suffer from rheumatism and troublesome knee joints. Nature's way of telling us that the **LEGS** of today simply aren't up to scratch. New modern legs will see knees replaced by telescopic, spring loaded joints, enabling man to leap, kangaroo-like, over huge distances at speeds of up to 300 miles per hour. Our **FEET** and **ANKLES** will look more like aeroplane undercarriages than the smelly and uncomfortable contraptions we walk on today. Axles will replace creaking ankle joints, and smooth running caster wheels will spring up where once we had toes.

BARNSLEY

It's hard to believe that in the course of time such incredibly complex physical change can take place. But these developments are nothing compared to those which have already occured over man's brief history on Earth. We cannot hope to ever fully understand nature. We can but marvel at this incredible evolutionary balancing act that we call life.

What the stars think...

We decided to ask a few well-known celebrities how they'd react to meeting the Man Of The Future.

Bubbly 'Hi-De-Hi' actress **SUE POLLARD**, alias "Miss Cathcart", wasn't in when we called, however a spokesman revealed that Miss Pollard was fully booked until Christmas, and could be seen starring in Dick Whittington at the Bristol Hippodrome until the end of the season.

"No I would not", said former British motor racing champ **JACKIE STEWART** when asked whether he'd like to race against the man of the future. Jackie's racing driver son Paul may well be more enthusiastic, but he was unavailable for comment.

American pop Queen **DONNA SUMMER**, recently back in the charts with hits like 'I Don't Wanna Get Hurt' and 'Love's About To Change', was saying nothing. "This whole thing sounds rather childish and far-fetched," a spokesman for her record company told us.

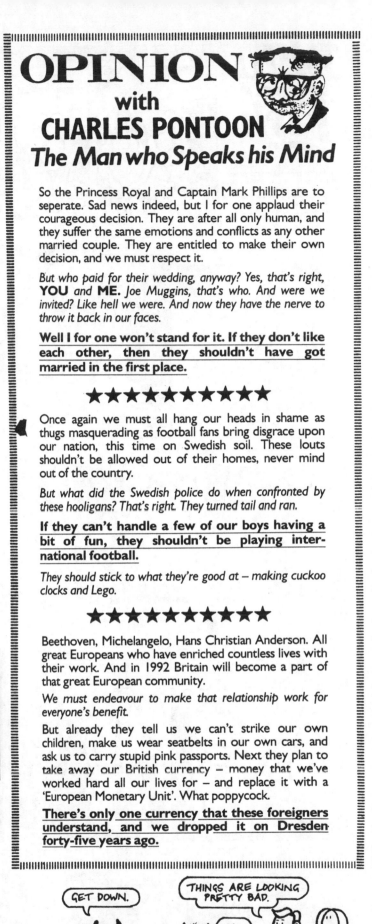

15

17

21

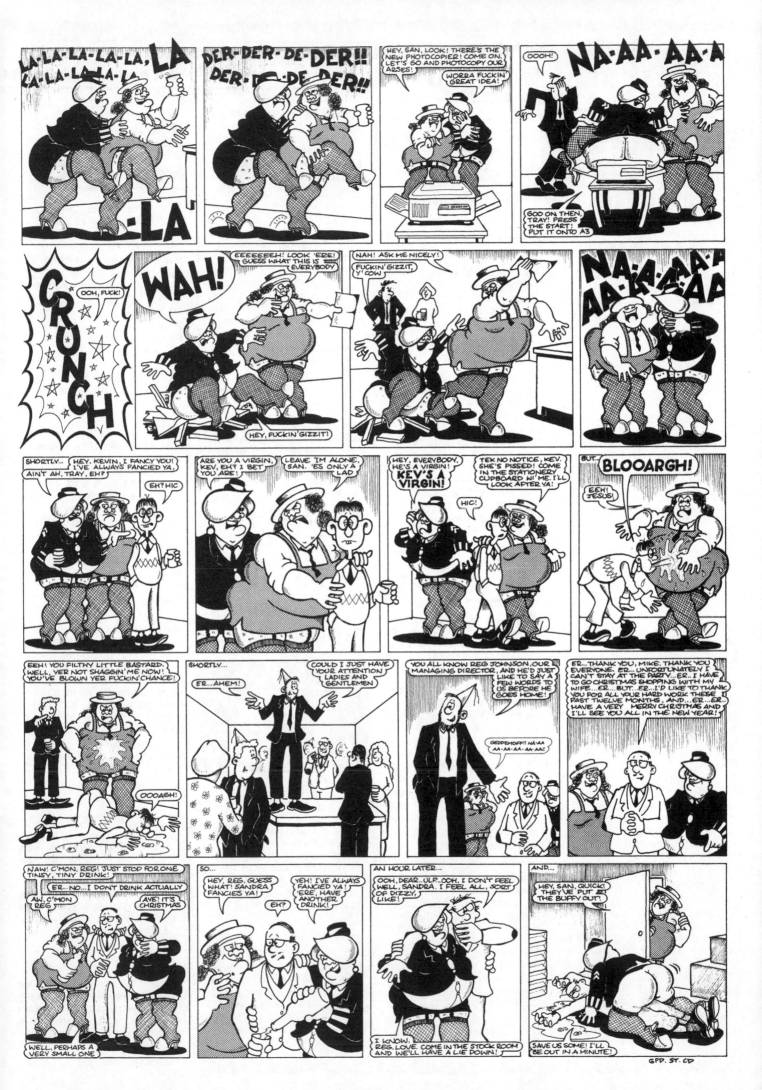

LeTTERbOckSo

Viz
LetterBocks
P.O. Bocks 1PT
Newcastle upon Tyne
NE99 1PT.

Rolling in the aisles

At my father's funeral the other day, the bottom fell out of the coffin and the body smashed onto the marble church floor. Unfortunately the head became separated and rolled under one of the pews, whence it became stuck under a wooden panel. Everyone was in fits of laughter as the vicar took half an hour to retrieve the head using a candlestick. Even the undertaker couldn't keep a straight face. Had my father been alive, I'm sure he would have been laughing as loud as we were.

D. Spruce
Reading

They say you can't have your cake and eat it. What a load of crap. Only the other day I saw a boy who had a large cream cake which he promptly ate.

Conor Jameson
Stirling

Last week I went to a football match. It was a great game, end to end stuff for ninety minutes. It was two goals each with a minute to play when incredibly, the referee turned down a penalty. "Open your eyes ref", I shouted. "Are you blind or something?". Then suddenly I remembered – I was the referee!

K. G. Jenkins
Doncaster

My husband and I were both fed up with buying electrical appliances only to find that no plug was supplied. So we emigrated to Canada. Over here even the cheapest item comes with a plug already attached.

Mrs. S. Hall
Ontario

Three cheers for British Telecom Directory Enquiries. Every time I phone them, they know the number. At best, I can only remember 5 or 6.

Ian Vallance
London

Every evening I go in the street and watch the six o'clock news through my neighbour's front room window, since I don't own a TV of my own. However, since I am unable to lip read I suggested that he might consider buying a teletext set. Imagine my dismay when he knocked eight of my teeth out.

K. Brett
Brentwood

Fair deal for OAPs

I have a solution to the problem of Britain's inadequate old age pensions, currently a meagre £43 per week. Why don't the Government increase this amount to £100, but pay it monthly instead of weekly. This way they'll actually save money. The dotty old pensioners will be delighted with their new hand out, and probably won't notice the change in frequency.

V. Fleming
Bristol

Congratulations on your 10th Anniversary issue. It's another corker – the funniest one yet. My husband and I have been reading Viz for the last ten years and have never missed a single issue, apart from numbers 1-35. Mind you, it's not as funny as it used to be.

Mrs. E. Hartnell
Wembley

What is the point of testing nuclear bombs underground? We don't fight wars there. Why not test them in real conditions, like over Paris or Belgium.

D. Bull
Devon

As a travelling salesman I often have the misfortune to hit and kill small animals while travelling on the roads at night. I always stop and pop the poor victim into the boot of my car. Eventually I hope to have enough of them saved up to make a small coat or jacket for my wife.

Mr. P. Parker
Preston

Grandson is a monster

My husband and I were looking forward to the birth of our first grandchild. So you can imagine our disappointment when my daughter gave birth to a baby that can only be described as "ugly".

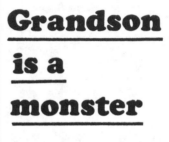

As you'll see from the enclosed picture, after two months our grandson's appearance has not improved. I wonder whether any other readers have unattractive babies?

Mrs. G. Evans
Gleneagles

★*Do you know someone who has an unattractive baby or young child? Send a photo of them to our usual address, and remember to mark your envelope "Ugly Children". There's a tenner for the ugliest tot!*

It's a sell out

It's a complete disgrace that you had so much advertising in your latest issue. What a shame to see you dirtying your hands with money from these big commercial organisations. Don't think your readers are fooled.

A. Scattock
Family Butcher
The High Street
Givenchester
Open 9-5 Mon.-Sat. "The tastiest cuts – and a sausage with a smile".

Thanks to the boy who shot and killed my cat, Tammy with an air gun last week. Little did he know Tammy had cataracts in both eyes, and sooner or later I was going to have to pay a vet to have her destroyed. This youth's malicious act has saved me a few pounds, much needed at this time of year.

Mrs. P. Hartside
Rochdale

My elderly mother is blind and for each birthday I gave her a small piece of newspaper, telling her it was a £50 note. She has been saving these in a tin for years intending to go on holiday. Imagine my despair when she had a successful cataract operation and promptly cut me out of her will.

A. Lovick
Newmarket

«top

DON'T throw away disposable razors. Keep them in the kitchen, they're ideal for peeling potatoes.

P. J. Rudock
Nottingham

DON'T waste money on first class stamps. Simply write your letters a few days earlier and send them second class.

P. Honk
Leamington Spar

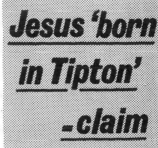

Jesus 'born in Tipton' -claim

Jesus wasn't born in Bethlehem – he was born in Tipton.

So says West Midlands Tourist chief Hugo Guthrie. He claims that the Bible got it wrong, and that Jesus was born not in a stable, but in a lock-up garage on the outskirts of Tipton town centre.

STAR

"The Bible will have to be re-written", says Mr Guthrie, who's case hinges on an ancient newspaper cutting he discovered which reported the birth in detail. "It also spoke of a star which appeared above the Tipton area on the night in question", said Mr Guthrie. Unfortunately he has since lost the newspaper cutting, however he is convinced that his version of events is true.

BETHLEHEM

"Joseph and Mary were probably travelling to Birmingham, which sounds a bit like Bethlehem, hence the mix up", Mr Guthrie explained. "Unfortunately in those days there was a lack of tourist accommodation in the West Midlands area, and consequently they were forced to spend the night in a cold, damp garage. The rest, as the say, is history".

Nowadays things have improved, and Mr Guthrie claims there is first class accommodation plus a warm welcome waiting for the many tourists and pilgrims whom he expects will flock to Tipton in the light of his revelations.

TALKS

Mr Guthrie is already involved in talks with Tipton Parish Council about funding for a proposed monument to mark the exact spot where Christ was born. In the meantime Tipton Tourist Board will be going ahead with plans to produce a full colour brochure entitled "Tipton – Birth Place of Christ", which will be available from libraries, post offices and public swimming baths in the West Midlands area.

TIPS »

SAVE on expensive washing powder by stealing your neighbours' clean washing from the line.
E. K. Wright
Ashington

AVOID complete misery and possible suicide by moving away from Luton, Bedfordshire.
Martin Roberts
Luton

DRILL a one inch hole in the door of your refrigerator. This will allow you to check that the light goes off when you close the door.
T. Baccus
Cheltenham

FOOL neighbours into thinking your car has an expensive alarm fitted by sleeping in it each night and sounding the horn for one minute at regular intervals.
M. Planck
Stafford

NEXT time you're at the seaside try turning your greenhouse upside down and fitting an outboard motor. The kids will be kept occupied for hours viewing the fascinating underwater flora and colourful fish.
M. Thresher
Bristol

STOP your canary from flying around its cage by placing bulldog clips on each of its wings.
M. Faraday
Barking

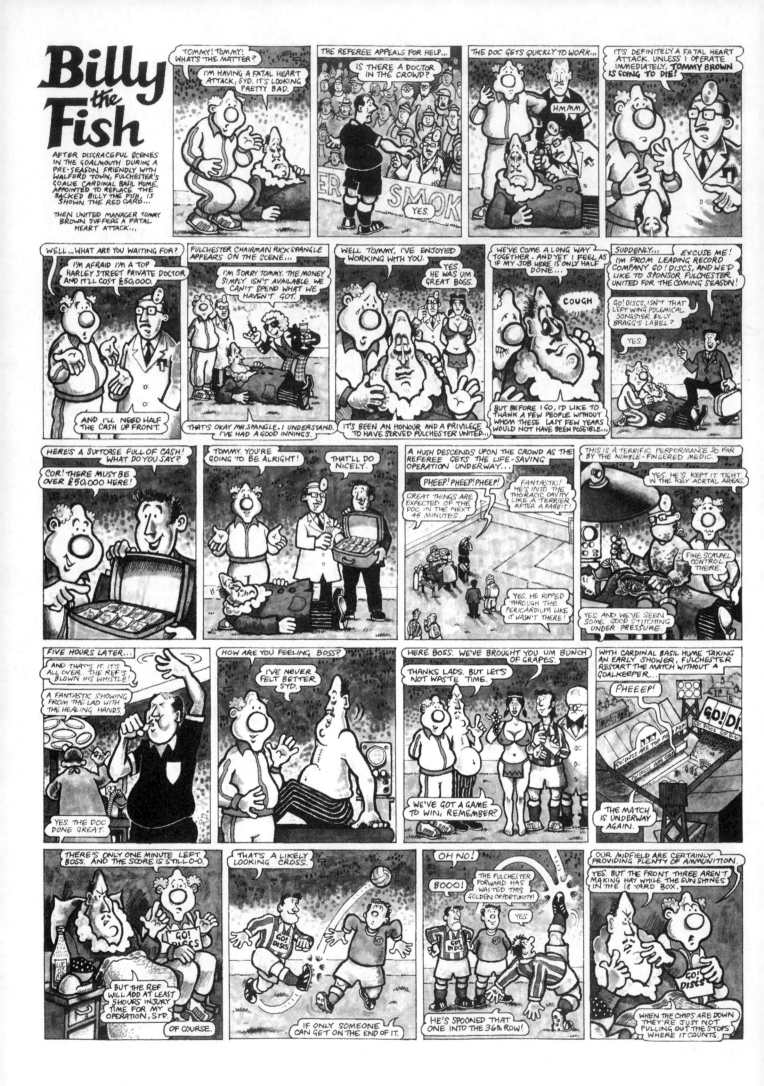

29

SPENT! SPENT! SPENT!

'And now I'm skint' says pools win Trev

A Shrewsbury man claims he is flat broke — only months after celebrating a fairytale win on the pools.

Joy soon turned to sorrow for Trevor Singleton, and his wife Barbara, when their dream success on the pools suddenly became a nightmare.

"Winning the pools was the worst thing that ever happened to us", said Trevor, 46. "I wish I'd never set eyes on the money. It's brought us nothing but heartache".

JACKPOT

The Singleton's couldn't believe their luck when a pools official arrived on the doorstep of their two bedroomed terrace house with the news that they'd won an incredible £312. "I couldn't even remember filling in the coupon", Trevor told us. Immediately the celebrations – and the spending – began.

WINDFALL

"We went out and we spent, spent, spent. We'd never had money before, and we were throwing it about like confetti. In one week alone we bought a new vacuum cleaner, a new Thermos flask for work, and had our toaster repaired. We were spending like there was no tomorrow".

FORTUNE

Soon Trevor resigned from his job as Allotment Supervisor for the local council. Then, after news of their good fortune appeared in the Shrewsbury and Wellington Bugle, begging letters began to arrive. "Suddenly everyone needed money. Friends, relatives, even total strangers were asking for cash. And like a fool I gave them it", he recalls.

BONANZA

Meanwhile the lavish spending continued. Trevor's wife Barbara returned home one day to find a brand new cover on her ironing board, while in the garden Trevor splashed out on a new paraffin heater for his greenhouse, and some seed trays.

EXCLUSIVE

"It was only the best for me. No expense spared. I was living like a King, thinking it would last forever".

THE VIRGINIAN

Although he didn't realise it, the money was dwindling rapidly. Trevor continues, "I was going out at nights and buying drinks for my mates. On one occasion I even paid for a taxi home. I was loving every minute of it". But the real problems started when Trevor began to gamble.

Mr Singleton today – "I wish I'd never seen the money."

"I'd never gambled in my life. But one night I spotted a fruit machine in the pub, and that was it. Before I knew what has happened I'd stuffed £1.60 into it, and I had no change left at all. I had to go to the bar to get some more. By the end of the evening I must have lost over £2.50. When I awoke the next morning I was physically sick".

HIGH CHAPARAL

Only months after receiving his cheque, Trevor had squandered the lot. He insists that every penny has been spent, and all he has left to show for it is a pile of unpaid bills. "I'm up to my neck in debt now", he confessed, fighting back the tears. "I owe the newsagent for two weeks' papers, and I've had a final reminder for my phone bill which is £27. I'm flat broke. Apart from a small amount my wife and I have saved in a building society, we haven't got a penny to our names".

LANCER

Yet despite it all, Trevor admits that if he won the pools tomorrow he'd probably do the same again. "I must admit, I enjoyed it while it lasted", he told us.

GUNSMOKE

Now unemployed, and living on meagre social security hand-outs, Trevor's only real regret is not taking his wife on the dream holiday they had planned. "We'd always talked about going on a caravan holiday in Wales, as my wife has relatives in the area", he told us. "This was our once-in-a-lifetime chance to visit them. But now it looks like we never will".

Flashback to happier times – Mr Singleton celebrates his jackpot with wife Barbara and friends.

Garage gets Royal blessing

By Reg Dildo

A Dudley man's plans to build a 'lean to' garage in the back yard of his terraced home have received the Royal seal of approval, from Prince Charles.

GARAGE

Bob Chambers plans to build the garage to house his car, gardening tools and other equipment. But before going ahead he hit upon the idea of writing to Prince Charles seeking Royal approval for the venture. Bob sent the Prince a sketch he had prepared of the proposed garage.

GARAGE

"To my surprise the Prince wrote back thanking me for the plan, and wishing me the best of luck with my garage," a delighted Bob told us.

GARAGE

Bob hopes to have the garage, which will be built of wood and corrugated iron, complete in time for Christmas.

MORE NAKED CRIME-FIGHTING THRILLS IN THE NEXT ISSUE!

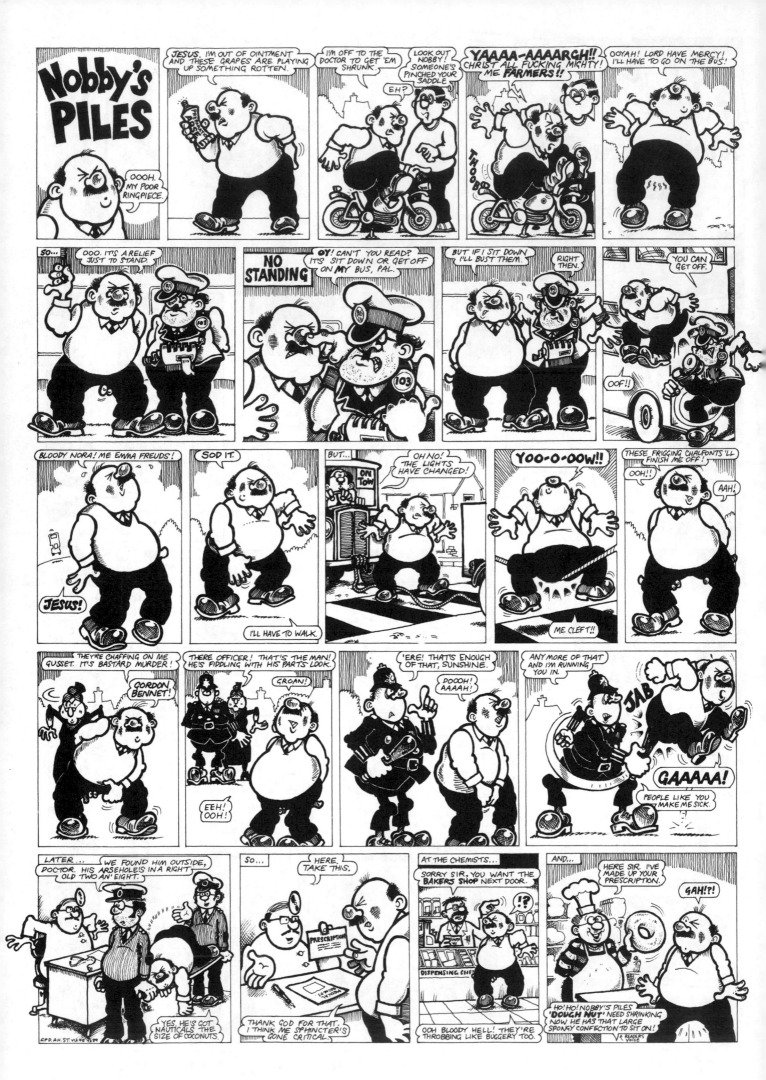

34

35

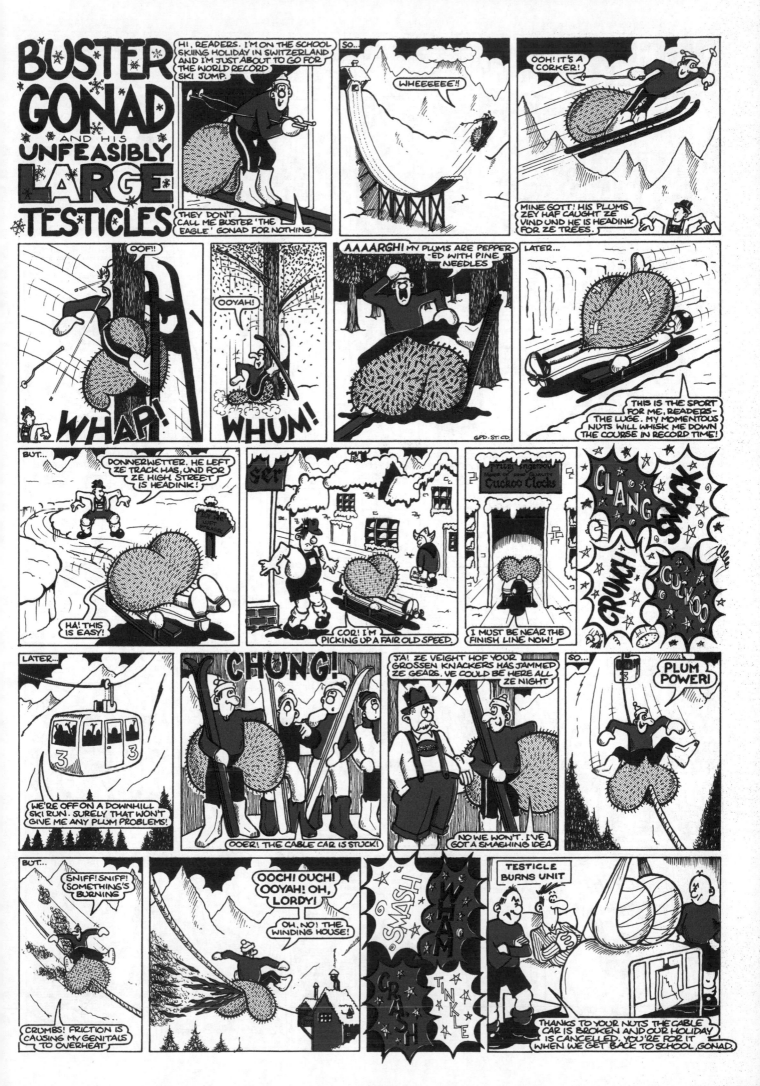

41

43

46

55

64

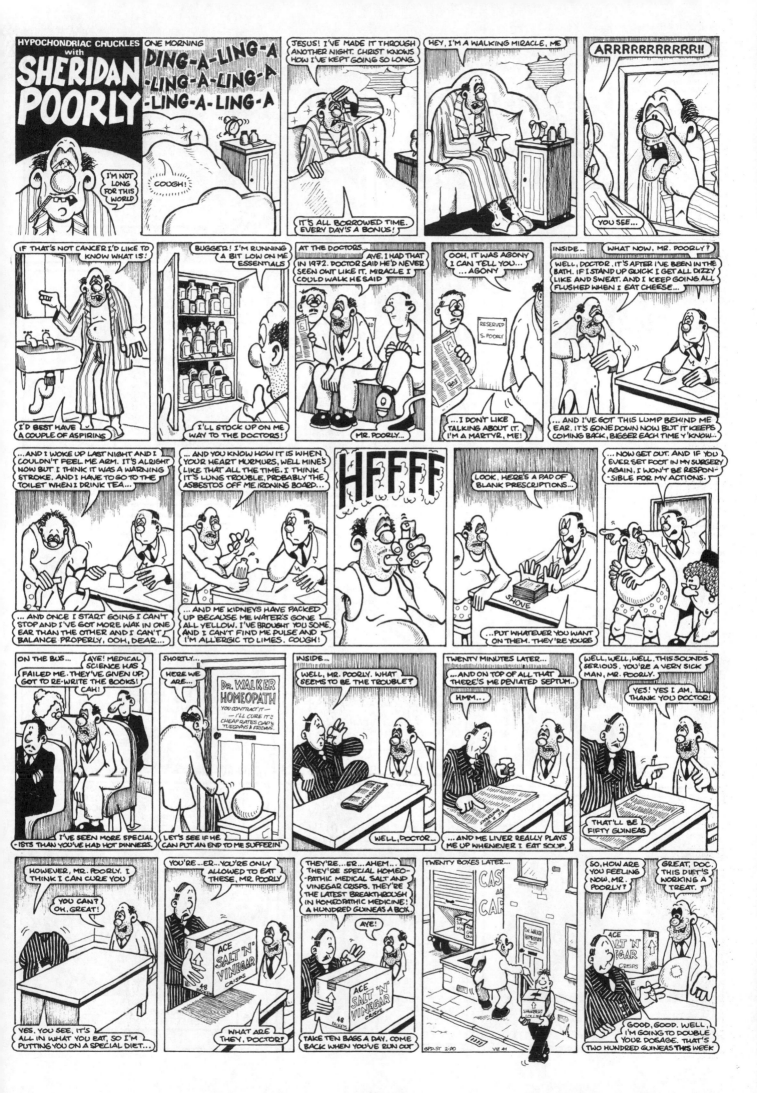

67

DO YOU DARES

Fancy yourself as an elite, highly trained killing machine?

Dressed to kill – an SAS soldier armed with the latest anti-terrorist Embassy storming equipment.

Who can honestly say that at some time or other they have not dreamt of joining the SAS – their motto "Who Dares Wins" – the crack force of highly trained soldiers feared by terrorists and enemies of Britain throughout the world.

But how many of us have got what it takes to join the SAS? Soldiers who apply to join the regiment must undergo many months of tough training, and some of the toughest applicants fall by the wayside. Only a handful are hard enough to join the SAS. So what are your chances of making the grade? Before you consider applying to join the SAS, try completing the following questionnaire.

Answer each question a, b, or c, then tot up your final score to reveal whether you've got what it takes.

Who dares wins – the SAS storming an Embassy yesterday.

1. You set off on a caravan holiday to Cornwall, but your car breaks down with 200 miles to go. What would you do?
a. Call the AA or RAC. It may be a loose connection, or the points may need adjusting.
b. Cancel your trip and return home by train or bus disappointed.
c. Pack the entire contents of the caravan into a rucksack and yomp the rest of the way, taking the most mountainous route available.

2. You have gone to stay with a friend who is getting married the next day, however when you arrive he has no spare beds in his house, and a relative is sleeping on the settee. What would you do?
a. Book into a nearby bed and breakfast.
b. Wrap up well and sleep in your car.
c. Smear your face in animal droppings, and go and live in a nearby forest for a week, feeding on nuts, berries and hunting wild animals.

3. You go shopping for some new clothes. There is a good selection in the shop. Which of the following outfits would you choose?
a. A smart but casual jacket, corduroy trousers and a paisley tie.
b. A pair of comfortable cricket flannels or slacks, and a lambswool v-neck sweater.
c. Black trousers, black roll-neck sweater, black balaclava, bullet-proof vest, lightweight boots and a gas-mask.

4. You begin to notice that your next-door neighbour is coming and going at strange hours of the day and night. You suspect therefore that he may be an international terrorist. What would you do?
a. Mind you own business. It's none of your concern.
b. Ask discreetly around the neighbourhood in order to put your mind at rest.
c. Smear your face with animal droppings and hide in a pile of mossy twigs in his back garden for six weeks, compiling a detailed dossier of his movements.

5. You are in a baker's shop when you notice an important foreign diplomat purchasing a Belgian bun and half a dozen finger rolls. Suddenly an Arab terrorist steps forward brandishing a semi-automatic pistol. What would you do?
a. Dive for cover behind the pastry counter.
b. Lie flat on the floor and do exactly as you are told.
c. Swiftly disarm the terrorist using martial art skills before breaking his neck with your bare hands alone, and then dive on top of the diplomat to protect him until the police arrive.

6. You arrive at a restaurant for a meal, but are told by the head waiter that no tables are available for a least twenty minutes. What would you do?
a. Sit down and enjoy a drink until your table is ready.
b. Go to another restaurant that isn't quite so busy.
c. Smear your face in animal droppings, then throw a flash bomb into the salad bar before dragging everyone outside and forcing them at gunpoint to lie down in the car park, then return to pick the table of your choice.

72

WINS?

WHO DARES WINS

7. Your neighbour has asked you to look after his six thoroughbred dogs while he is on holiday. However, after a couple of days one dog is off his food and looks a little unwell. What would you do?
a. Ignore it. It's probably just pining for it's master.
b. Take it to the vets for a check-up. It's better to be on the safe side.
c. Take the dog to nearby waste ground, put a pillow over it's head and shoot it. Then return and kill all the remaining dogs to make sure you got the right one.

8. You pop round to a friend's house to see if he wants to go out for a drink. However, when you get there, there is no answer and the door is slightly ajar. What would you do?
a. Return home, and call back later.
b. Nip round the back to see if he's in the garden.
c. Burst into the house keeping your back to the wall and go from room to room, spraying the walls with bullets and occasionally doing a forward roll.

9. Whilst shopping in the supermarket an old lady catches your ankle with her trolley. When you get to the checkout you notice that the skin is slightly broken. What would you do?
a. Just forget it. It's only a scratch and it will heal itself in due course.
b. Nip back to purchase some elastoplast and some antiseptic cream.
c. Hastely improvise a makeshift field hospital in the fruit and vegetable section, and sever your leg below the knee using your Swiss army knife, then seal up the stump with a red hot iron, in case it goes septic.

10. You arrive home from work only to find that you have lost your house keys. You try the doors and windows but they are all locked securely. What would you do?
a. Return to work to look for your keys. If you cannot find them you can sleep in the office for the night.
b. Pop to a friend's house nearby until your wife returns. She has her own set of keys.
c. Smear your face in animal droppings, before busting into a neighbour's house using a sledgehammer. Leave the occupants bound and gagged in a downstairs room, then make your way up to the attic and remove a skylight before clambering along the roof towards your house, tying a rope round your chimney, absailing down your back wall and crashing in through a second floor window.

HOW DID YOU DO?

Award yourself one point for every answer a, two points for a b, and three points for each answer c.

Less than 10:—*Oh dear me. You'd be better suited to joining Dad's Army than the SAS. But don't worry – the TA would love to hear from you.*

11 to 20:—*Not a bad result. You're tough, but not quite tough enough. There could still be a career for you in the Royal Marines or the Parachute Regiment.*

21 to 30:—*Congratulations! You've got what it takes. Next time the SAS storm the Iranian Embassy* **YOU** *could be the first one in. Hurry down to your army careers office immediately and ask for an SAS application form.*

THEY'RE AT IT AGAIN ~ claims Ron

Billions of pounds being wasted on the construction of the Channel Tunnel should be spent on preparing Britain for war. For German plans to begin World War III are already well underway.

This is the startling claim being made by keen amateur historian Ronald Windthorpe who believes the German surrender of 1945 isn't worth the paper it's written on. And while Britain prepares to do business with her colleagues in 1992, Mr Windthorpe believes the Germans are building towards another blitz. "Jerry's a sly old fox", he told us, speaking from the air raid shelter in the back garden of his Lincolnshire home. "He's been quiet for too long. He's up to something, and this time we better be prepared for it".

HUN

"We should have learnt our lessons in '39 when Jerry caught us with our pants down", said Mr Windthorpe. "This time we should be ready for them, because if we aren't, we may find ourselves on the losing side".

BOSH

According to Mr Windthorpe dramatic measures must be taken immediately, among them the re-introduction of conscription, food rationing and the internment of all foreign nationals living in Britain. In the face of Government apathy, it has been left to Mr Windthorpe to fight a lone battle against the Bosh, and he has soldiered on bravely with his own preparations. Every morning he cycles two miles to the nearby seaside town of Mablethorpe to scan the horizon for signs of an enemy invasion. And he insists his wife, Joan, carries her gas mask with her at all times. The Windthorpes' two children, Sarah, 24, and Michael, 29, have been staying with an aunt in Wales since 1972.

SQUAREHEADS

There are several ways in which we can prepare ourselves for the advent of war, and Mr Windthorpe recommends that everyone adopts the following simple measures in order to protect themselves and their families.

* Fit blackout curtains to all windows, including skylights, and at night cover your car headlights so that they cannot be seen.

* Stick masking tape onto windows in the shape of a cross

* Build a bomb shelter in the garden by leaning sheets of wood against a kitchen table, and then building up a layer of sandbags around it.

Unfortunately, Mr Windthorpe's war efforts have come to a temporary standstill as he is currently awaiting sentence, having pleaded guilty at Cleethorpes magistrates court to a charge of theft after he was caught removing a road sign from the hard shoulder of the M62 near Goole. He asked for 362 similar offences to be taken into consideration. Sentence has been deferred pending psychiatric reports.

1939 and Jerry sets off for Poland.

LETTERBOCKS

I hit man's erection with hammer

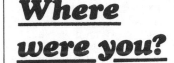

Letter Bocks
P.O. Bocks 1PT
Newcasel on Tine
Ne99 1pt

The other day my next door neighbour erected a brand new greenhouse in his garden. Immediately I took a sledgehammer and smashed it to pieces.

As I explained to the police, how can anyone be so irresponsible – surely my neighbour has heard of the effect of greenhouses on the ozone layer.

Martyn Pitt
Gloucester

I was convinced my husband was having an affair with his secretary, as he often returned home late from work. So I confronted him.

I felt such a fool when he reminded me he doesn't have a secretary – he's a bus driver, and had been working evening shifts.

Mrs C. Kettledrum
Filey

Vocabulary criticism

My 2 year old son fell in the park, grazing his knee quite badly. "Bums", exclaimed the cheeky scamp.

Imagine my surprise when a passing gentleman scolded him, saying that bad language is the last resort of a limited vocabulary. How ridiculous. What choice of words does a 2 year old have? The silly old fucker.

P. McLavin
Fife

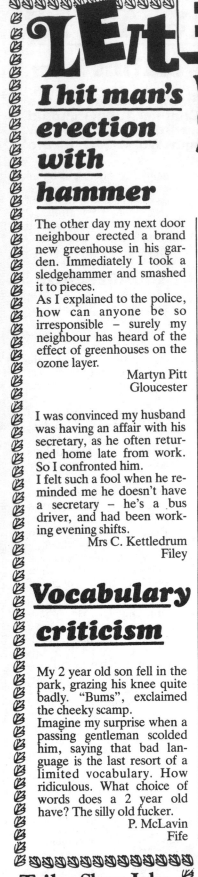

Tailor Shop Joke

Things today aren't as well made as they used to be. I have owned the same mop for over 40 years. In all that time it has only required three new heads, and two new handles.

J. Aldbury
Oldham

Where were you?

It seems that everyone can remember what they were doing when President Kennedy was killed, but what about Harry Worth? He died only last year, and it would be interesting to hear whether readers can recall how they were occupied at the time.

J. Askew
Lincoln

I am sick up to the back teeth with lefty do-gooders lecturing us about the environment. In my day people were too busy earning a living to worry about such things. The problem with people today is that they have everything too easy.

Major Percy Reid
Berwickshire

Marvellous memories

I remember the Coronation in 1953. We kids had a marvellous time at our street party. Wouldn't it be nice if the Queen died so that we could have another.

J. Askey
Bournemouth

I was interested to read Mr Blackett-Ord's experience (Viz 38) when he mistook his slipper for a beetle.

Sitting listening to a record, I noticed something move on the floor in front of me. I reached down to pick it up, only to find out it was my foot!

I had been tapping it in tune to the music.

R. Emmerson
Kent

How about a picture of a bird dancing with her tits out?

Tom McArthur
Bolton

Here you are Tom. Happy to oblige. Do any other readers have special requests? Write and tell us what YOU'D like to see on Britain's brightest letters page.

If you ask me Paul Daniels' so-called 'magic' is a total fraud. After all, if he was a **real** magician he could just say "Allez oop!" and grow a full head of hair.

Tony Pickles
Burton-on-Trent

Make your minds up

These so-called 'experts' make me sick. First they tell us old folk to keep warm, then they complain that the world is getting too hot because of this 'greenhouse' effect. Why don't they make up their minds.

J. Alden
Market Harborough

Why not put the price of Viz up? £1 is a much rounder figure, and readers will no longer have to hang around in draughty newsagents shops waiting for change from their £1 coin.

Mr I. Coxhall
Bedford

That's an interesting idea, Mr Coxhall.

I have recently noticed that, during the evenings it gets dark, but come the following morning it is light again. Are we witnessing the greenhouse effect already?

M. Peters
West Ham

TOP TIPS

AVOID jet lag by simply taking an earlier flight, thus arriving fully refreshed and on time.

Sgt. R. J. Crowe
662 Squadron, Germany

PUT A STOP to car thieves by syphoning off all your petrol whenever you park your car, and carrying it round with you in one or two plastic buckets.

D. Griffiths
Kent

USED matchsticks, when sharpened with a penknife, are ideal for picking up small pieces of cheese, or cocktail sausages.

S. Jones
Edinburgh

DON'T throw away odd pieces of string which are too short. Knot them together to produce a new and useful piece of string.

Sam Evans
Shropshire

ROBIN HOOD 'FROM TIPTON'-CLAIM

Modern historians are divided over the popular legend of Robin Hood. Some believe it is based on historical fact, while others dismiss it as pure fiction.

But recent research has cast new light on the subject, and one man believes he has now solved the mystery.

EXCLUSIVE
By our West Midlands Correspondent

Mr. Guthrie yesterday

Hugo Guthrie was recently appointed Senior Archivist by Tipton Borough Council, and his subsequent research into the legend reveals that Robin and his Merry Men did live many years ago, but not in Sherwood Forest. According to Mr Guthrie's findings they lived 50 miles away, near Tipton in the West Midlands.

WOOD

"There was a small wooded area south west of Tipton called Gornalwood", Mr Guthrie explained. "In medieval times this was the home of Robin Hood and his band of merry men. Contrary to popular misconceptions, all Robin's adventures took place in and around the Tipton area, in places like Dudley, Sedgley and Kingswinford."

CASTLE

According to Mr Guthrie, Robin's arch enemy the Sherriff of Nottingham didn't exist. "Nottingham is a corruption of the word Netherton, a small town ten miles south of Tipton. It was there, at Netherton Castle, Robin was often held prisoner by the evil Sherriff of Netherton. And it was here also that he later met and married Maid Marion, who was from the West Bromich area".

HAMPER

Unfortunately nothing remains of the castle, and all records of its existance have been destroyed over the years. Indeed Mr Guthrie's research has been hampered by a lack of historical evidence. "Many of the records dating from that period have been lost. In medieval days local councils were notoriously bad at record keeping. And in any case Oliver Cromwell burnt them all", he told us. So Mr Guthrie has had to rely heavily on word of mouth, talking to many locals and old folk in the Tipton area. "Many old people produced photo albums and scrap books which were invaluable to my research", he told us.

Unlike Netherton Castle, a small forest still stands at Gornalwood, and Mr Guthrie believes he has pin-pointed the exact tree that Robin Hood lived in. "I'm afraid the legend of the Major Oak is a load of rubbish", he told us. "The actual tree is a small conifer, but it has great historical significance and should become a popular tourist attraction".

PICNIC BASKET

As Chairman of the Tipton Tourist Committee Mr Guthrie is only too well aware of the commercial potential of this new found heritage. And plans are afoot to build a Robin Hood Visitors Centre adjacent to the historic tree on land which, ironically, is owned by Mr Guthrie's brother-in-law.

DEVELOPMENT

"I can see this development bringing flocks of tourists to Tipton in the nineties", said Mr Guthrie, who plans to celebrate the official opening of the Robin Hood Heritage Centre with a 'Robin Hood Weekend'.

BIG STICKS

Visitors to Tipton will be able to enjoy traditional medieval morris dancing by the Stourbridge Stompers, an archery display by the West Midlands under 25s 1986 longbow champion Ron Pilkington, plus a full scale re-enactment of the historic fight with big sticks between Little John and Robin Hood, which took place on a narrow footbridge over the Staffordshire and Worcestershire Canal.

MAKE your neighbours think you've had a house fire by blackening your windows with shoe polish, and throwing your matresses out into the garden.
F. Lee
Manchester

SAVE time and hot water in the morning by popping your cold, damp facecloth into the microwave.
P. Wilson
Troon

AMUSE your children by dressing up as a circus clown and performing card tricks over breakfast.
I. Beadle
Dartford

PREVENT your cold from spreading by placing a stout paper bag over your head. When finished with it, don't throw the bag away. It will be ideal for storing odd bits and pieces.
S. Evans
Ruddington

A WIRE paperclip, unfolded, is ideal for picking up small pieces of cheese and cocktail sausages.
S. Jones
Edinburgh

PUT BLUE food colouring into your drink at the pub. Invariably people will ask you what you're drinking, and the liklihood of your drink being stolen when you visit the toilet is greatly reduced.
B. Reedsmouth
Hawick

TAKE a tip from bank robbers. Leave the engine of your car running when going into a shop to buy frozen vegetables. Making a 'quick get-away' will reduce the risk of them thawing before you get home.
Mrs G. Walton
Holmfirth

DOCTOR. THERE'S SOME SORT OF BUG GOING ROUND

EXPOSED! SECRET

Behind the scenes drama of Britain's favourite soap

Coronation Street is Britain's most popular TV soap. Yet, according to one insider the **REAL LIFE** drama that goes on behind the scenes of "The Street" is more exciting than the soap itself. "You wouldn't believe the goings on", Street star Sidney Blenkinsop has told us.

Sidney first appeared in Britain's longest running soap as long ago as 1968 when viewers briefly saw him sit quietly in a corner of the Rovers Return. Since then he's become a regular appearing many times in the Rovers and on one occasion actually ordering drinks. Over the years he's got to know the stars better than anyone, and now for the first time he blows the lid off Britain's longest running soap.

EXCLUSIVE
By Street star Sid

❛ Granada TV pay writers a fortune to invent storylines for the Street. But the most exciting stories of all are the ones which go on behind the scenes. Viewers simply wouldn't believe some of the episodes I've witnessed!

EYE

On screen many of the characters don't see eye to eye. That's what soaps are all about. Occasionally they come to blows, like the time when Mike Baldwin, alias actor Johnny Briggs, grappled with Ken Barlow outside Mike's factory. Of course they were acting. But you wouldn't believe some of the real life fisticuffs that go on. Usually its over something petty -- a disagreement about the script for example – but feet and furniture start flying, and it always ends up with at least one person in hospital. If you watch carefully you can always spot at least one of the actors with a black eye, and I don't think a single members of the cast has got a full set of teeth left.

BUNCH

You'd imagine the cast would be a tight knit friendly bunch. But I can tell you they're not. There's so much competition for the best lines, and endless arguments about who's going to say what. On set you can cut the atmosphere with a knife, and off it none of the actors ever speak to each other.

FAMILY

But despite the odd disagreements the Street stars are a great bunch to work with. We're like one big family, always looking out for each other. Like the time Roy Barraclough lost his wallet and we all stopped work to help him look for it.

If you ever think some of the plots that script writers dream up for the Street seem far fetched, you should see the kind of drama the stars get up to in real life. Hardly a day goes by without one star or another getting pregnant, having a love child or discovering that another star is their real father.

LOVE CHILD

I will never forget the day Chris Quinten turned up for work only to be told that Thelma Barlow, alias Mavis Riley was expecting his love child. Sparks were flying and her on-screen husband, actor Peter Baldwin threatened to kill him. Thelma told Chris she'd ruin him unless he handed over £250,000 to bring up the child. Chris's screen wife Gail Tilsley told him that Thelma would have to have an abortion, and her screen mother Audrey Roberts was taken to hospital in hysterics. Alf Roberts, alias actor Brian Mosley, Audrey's on-screen husband, armed himself with a gun and went out to shoot Quinten, his on-screen son-in-law, alias actor Brian Tilsley.

Gail Worth, alias actress Helen Tilsley, former on screen husband of actress Chris Quinten (alias actor Brian Tilsley).

In the end it all turned out be have been a big mistake. Someone had got a telephone message wrong, and nobody was pregnant after all. But that was quite an episode I can tell you.

Not many people know that Prince Charles is probably Coronation Street's biggest fan. Indeed if it wasn't for the Prince of Wales there wouldn't be a Street at all.

Charles – Street was his idea.

For when Granada TV first planned the series it was going to be set in a high rise block of flats called Coronation Court. But the Prince heard of their plans and wrote to them pointing out that the community spirit would be lost in an unsightly high rise building, and that elderly residents would be isolated, especially if the lifts didn't work. He suggested a traditional row of Victorian terraced houses instead. The producers agreed, and the idea of Coronation Street was born.

TOPLESS

The Street has for many years been Britain's most successful soap, however the producers panicked when the BBC's Eastenders soared to number one in the viewers' chart. They considered a number of crazy schemes to boost viewing figures. They even tried asking sexy barmaid Bet Lynch, alias actress Julie Goodyear to work topless behind the bar at the Rovers Return. But fortunately their letter to her was lost in the post, otherwise I'm sure she would have resigned in disgust.

DOCTOR. I'VE GOT A PAIN IN THE ARSE.

GYLES

Sidney (arrowed) as viewers often see him in the Street. In the foreground is the Rovers Return

Albert Tatlock got on the wrong side of Granada bosses by asking for a pay rise. When they turned him down actor Jack Howarth threatened to leave and join Eastenders instead. A week later he was dead.

TOP

Jack was just one of the many great actors who have appeared in the Street. Many of today's top stars began their acting career in the series, among them Davy Jones of pop group The Monkees.

Street pop star actor Monkey Jones.

It's a tribute to the actors that the viewers often imagine characters like Rita Fairclough, Jack Duckworth and Harry Cross as being real people. Every week Granada TV receive tons of mail addressed to these people, and the actors who play them are often approached by fans mistaking them for their on screen characters.

PARTS

But sometimes an actor can become so obsessed whith his part he can, without realising it, literally become the character he plays – 24 hours a day. It's a fascinating psychological condition, only recently discovered and quite unique to soap stars who can end up losing their own identity. Unfortunately however there aren't any examples of that I can think of. '

Next week: Frank Sinatra's Street connection, plus how detectives hunting the Yorkshire Ripper swooped on the Rovers Return.

Several new storylines were considered and a sizzling no holds barred sex scene between Ivy Tilsley and Don Brennan was filmed under tight security. No one was allowed on the set, but I crept to a window to take a look. It was red hot stuff, but they'd only been at it for 2 or 3 minutes when the window steamed up!

END

In the end ITV bosses insisted that the scene be cut, or the programme would have to go out after 11.00 p.m. Reluctantly they agreed to drop it.

ATTRACTIVE

Dirty Den was single handedly responsible for Eastenders' success. The ladies were switching to the BBC to watch him in their millions. So Street producers told actor Bernard Youens, who played Stan Ogden in the series, to lose weight in order to become more attractive to women.

DIED

But after months of unsuccessful dieting Bernard died, and the Street lost one of its brightest stars. No one can be blamed for his death, but I blame the producers.

KNOCKERS

It's easy to criticise the producers for the way they run the show. But they have a difficult job to do, and I would never knock them.

RELIEF

There were sighs of relief at Granada TV when Dirty Den eventually left Eastenders. BBC chiefs decided to have him bumped off by a gangland hit man. It was lucky for actor Leslie Grantham, alias Dirty Den character Queen Vic landlord Dennis Watts, that they did, because Granada bosses had been planning to do the job themselves – with real bullets. They had been making discreet enquiries about the availability of a real life hit man and had already got several quotes for the job.

SOAPY

Murder might seem a little far fetched, but in the crazy world of the soaps anything can happen. And sometimes it does.

Black BAG
THE FAITHFUL BORDER BIN LINER

Rab, Andrew's ram had gone missing again – but thanks to Bag's superb sense of smell they had managed to track him down.

Rab had wandered on ahead. He was attacking a boy he had found with his head stuck in a tree.

"Thank you for saving me", said the young lad. "I come from the Orphanage and I was looking for birds eggs."

"My, he's a fine bag", said the lad. "I've always dreamt of having a bag of my own."

Bag and Andrew walked the wee lad to the end of his road then set out to look for Rab, again.

"Merry Christmas bag", said Andrew, looking down at the dozing binliner. Then gently slipped him his Christmas stocking.

As they sat in the warm glow of the stove, Andrew's thoughts returned to the poor Orphan they had met. "We must do something to brighten up his Christmas", said Andrew.

With a heavy heart Andrew fingered his family's collection of man traps. He had decided to sell them and buy the wee fellow a Christmas present.

The next day was bright and clear as he set out for Peebles with his family treasures stowed in Black Bag.

81

TINKER, TAILOR, SOLDIER ...STAR!

By our Showbiz writers **PIERS LYING** and **GARY BASTARD**

Many of today's top celebrities have known what it is like to perform less glamourous jobs. Indeed the stars instantly recognisable for their recent TV success have usually spent many years in poorly paid and at times unusual occupations before making the big time. Here's just a few of the odd ways in which today's celebrities once earned their crust.

⭐ If you had the misfortune to lock yourself in the public toilets of Victoria Coach Station in 1964, you'd have been in for a big surprise. For you may well have been rescued by a short, familiar figure wearing distinctive spectacles. That's because in 1964 that man with the job of maintaining those lavatory doors was none other than top TV comedian **RONNIE CORBETT**! Toilet Door Maintenance Officer was just one of a string of part time jobs the pint-sized comic took on to earn extra cash while struggling to make it in the show-biz world. Nowadays,. with TV success like the Two Ronnies and Sorry to his name, and successful panto appearances under his belt, Ronnie can afford to sit back and spend his spare time pottering about in the garden.

⭐ *Residents of Grantham in Lincolnshire never knew what to expect when visiting their local dentist. Something of an eccentric, he would often hide in a cupboard for up to five minutes before springing out to shock his baffled patients. He was also well known for leaving a 'whoopee' cushion on his dentist's chair. And who was that now famous dentist? None other than zany TV prankster* **JEREMY BEADLE**. *Jester Jeremy quit dentistry in 1978 to become a full time TV funny man.*

⭐ **SIR ALLISTAIR BURNETT** has achieved a great deal in a marvellous career in news broadcasting. But it was only due to a stroke of luck that his news career got off the ground at all. In 1979 he had been working hundreds of feet above the streets of London – as a window cleaner. An alert news editor spotted him polishing the windows at the ITN offices. He was immediately offered a job as Senior Newscaster, but this came as such a shock that the luckless Sir Allistair lost his balance and fell 23 storeys, landing in a flower bed below. After a brief spell in hospital he eventually hung up his bucket and officially began work at ITN.

⭐ *It's hard to imagine our senior politicians working in mundane, everyday jobs. But 32 years ago one of today's top Tory cabinet ministers could have been found hundreds of feet below the Houses of Parliament, working on the London Underground! After a brief spell as ticket collector Deputy Prime Minister* **SIR GEOFFREY HOWE** *worked as a driver on the Victoria Line before he was sacked in 1983, after turning up for work drunk. Sir Geoffrey then set is sights on a career in politics and Mrs Thatcher's right-hand man hasn't looked back since.*

⭐ *Bubbly Hi-Di-Hi star* **SU POLLARD** *ignored advice from her parents and gave up a promising career as a Research Scientist in order to go on the stage. Former colleagues at the University of Cardiff Medical Research Institute were shocked by her decision to quit. After several years of research she was thought to have been only days away from inventing a cure for cancer. But in the end Su had the last laugh, becoming a big hit as the scatter-brained Miss Cathcart in Hi-Di-Hi.*

⭐ Were it not for his marriage to the Queen of England, **PRINCE PHILLIP**, the Duke of Edinburgh, would never have become a member of the royal family. He would have remained lowly Stourbridge rent collector, Phillip Tunstall. Before he met the Queen, Phillip had been collecting rent for Warwickshire County Council for several years. During that time, he was commended for bravery after thugs had tried to grab his rent bag. Have-a-go hero Phillip fought off the brutes, who were forced to flee empty-handed.

THIS SUPER PRIZE IS JUST THE JOB

Here's a chance for you to win a trip to the job centre of your choice, anywhere in the UK. We are offering first class travel tickets for two plus two nights' hotel accommodation at the destination of your choice, to the lucky winner of this fabulous 'job related' competition. All you have to do is read the celebrity CV below, then tell us which famous star you think it belongs to.

Born in Cardiff, his first job was as Butchers Boy, cycling around the valleys of South Wales delivering sausages. He then signed apprentice forms with Port Vale football club, eventually making seven appearances, scoring one goal. Left football to return to full-time education, taking a psychology degree at York University. Two years later while working as a lumberjack in Scotland a record company executive overheard him whistling and dancing to rock 'n' roll tunes. He was immediatey signed up and today he is surely Britain's brightest singing star.

Answers on a postcard please to Shakin' Stevens Celebrity CV Job Centre Visit Competition, Viz, PO Box 1PT, Newcastle upon Tyne, NE99 1PT. The competition closed on 31 March 1990. The winner waS notified by post shortly thereafter. Please remember to include your name, address and the name of the job centre which you would like to visit.

82

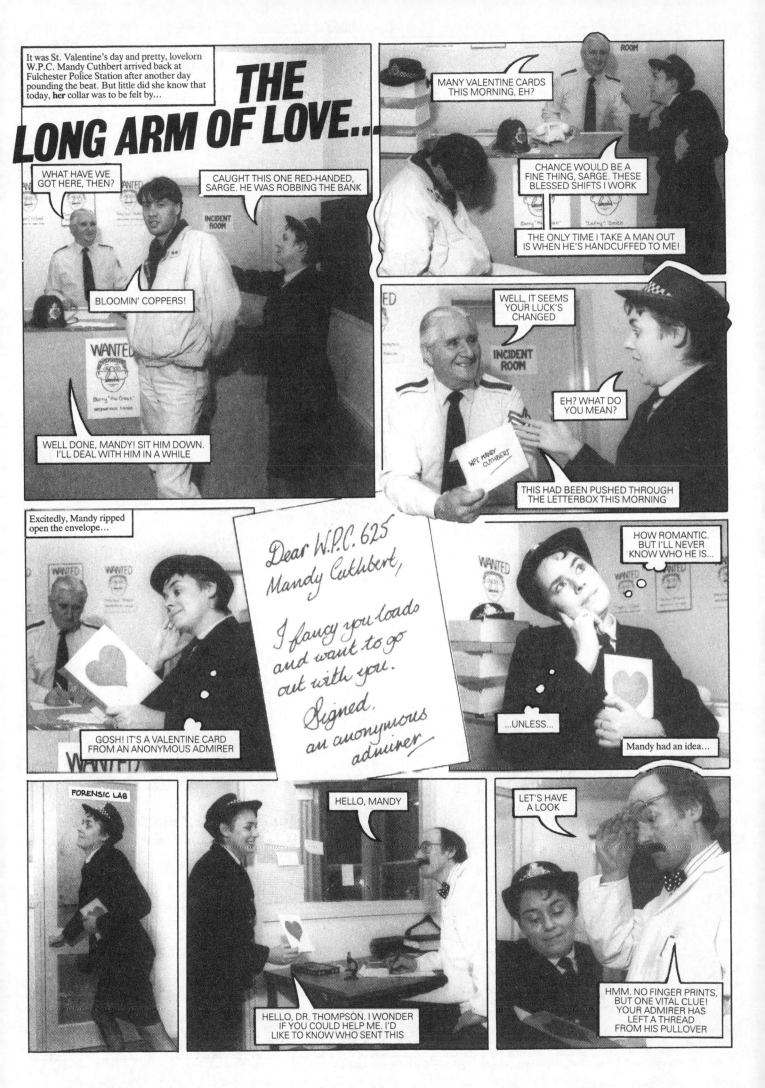

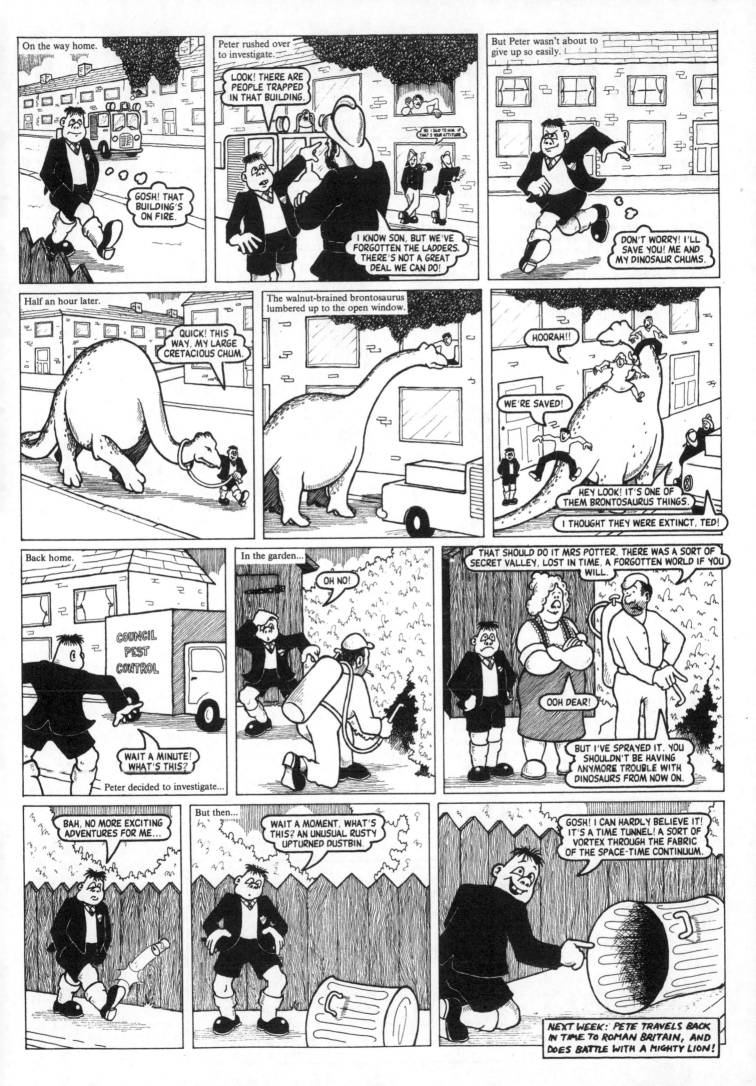

HOW GREEN A

The nineties are set to become the 'Green Decade' as we all become more aware of environmental issues. But do we?

Find out if you are 'environment friendly

Are you environment friendly? Do you care about the trees and plant life, or are flowers strictly for pansies? Do you agree with the growing number of people who fear that the earth's natural resources are being systematically exhausted to the irrevocable detriment of the environment, or don't you give a wank?

Here's your chance to find out. Just answer these key questions on the vital environmental issues, then tot up your score to find out just how **GREEN** you really are.

1 Whilst driving in the countryside you notice someone emptying drums of sulphuric acid into a stream. What would you do?
a. Join in the fun by emptying the contents of your car battery and watching the fish float up to the top.
b. Ignore them. It's none of your business.
c. Clamber aboard a precarious rubber dinghy and try to position yourself between the drums and the stream.

2 Whilst travelling on a bus you notice that the vehicle is pumping out toxic fumes into the atmosphere. What would you do?
a. Light up a cigarette, put your feet up on the seat in front of you sit back and enjoy your ride.
b. Make a mental note to travel by electric train next time.
c. Slap the driver and scream hysterically, refusing to pay your fare until the bus is converted to run on ozone free fuel.

3 Whilst on holiday in Brazil you notice a western developer attempting to ignite a rain forest, but his matches are damp. How would you react?
a. Lend him your cigarette lighter and some rolled up newspaper to get the fire going.
b. Ignore him. There's plenty of trees in Brazil – so what if he wants to burn a few.
c. Paint your face, take off your shoes and spend a week-end with a tribe of

Amazonian Indians before returning to Britain, going on Wogan, and making some crappy records. Then buy a house in California for seven million quid.

Sting

4 Whilst gardening you notice your next door neighbour working on his car. A trickle of oil is heading towards the gutter. What would you do?
a. Smile politely and continue spraying your shrubbery with a cocktail of Agent Orange, DDT and various industrial strength weed killers.
b. Don't worry about it. It will be drained away into the sea eventually.
c. Use your garden hosepipe to fashion a makeshift boom with which to contain the rapidly spreading slick

A new road cuts through the Brazilian rain forest.

before alerting the emergency services who will mount a massive 'Torrey Canyon' style clean-up operation.

5 During the night you are awoken by the sound of your neighbour attempting to dispose of his fridge. What would you do?
a. Get up and lend him your hacksaw to help get through all the pipes at the back.
b. Turn over and pretend to be asleep. It's none of your concern. The ozone layer is very big and it's only a small fridge anyway.
c. Dash out into the garden and deliver a closely argued and cogent lecture

over the garden fence, illustrated with slides and an overhead projector, on the dangers of CFC's and associated chemicals, before making a citizen's arrest and handing your neighbour over to the authorities in the morning.

6 You visit a well known fast food take away and purchase a Big Mac, six Chicken McNuggets with Barbecue Sauce, Regular Fries and a Filet-o-Fish. After eating your delicious meal what do you do with the convenient, attractive packaging?
a. Pull it into pieces and scatter them along the street. Any remaining bits can be burnt in your back garden along with old foam filled settees, plastic footballs, old tyres or the dashboard out of an Austin Princess, which you may happen to have lying around.
b. Leave it on the table to be disposed of by a member of the attractive, friendly and well paid staff.
c. Encase it in concrete and negotiate with the French Government to have it sent into space on the European rocket 'Ariane'.

7 You arrive home one rainy day and notice you don't have anywhere to put your umbrella. How would you solve this tricky problem?

a. Go on a safari holiday to Africa and shoot a family of elephants with a big gun. Then choose the best sized elephant's foot and hack it off to make an attractive umbrella stand for your hallway.

b. Shoot only one elephant, preferably an old or sick male. You will still have four feet to choose from.

c. Tranquilise an elephant and ask a professional vet to surgically remove one foot only and replace it with a wooden prosthesis. The elephant won't know the difference.

8 After relaxing in a deck chair on Blackpool beach you notice that the sea has risen by several feet due to global warming. What would you do?

a. Nothing. You live on a hill so your house won't be affected. Besides, you'll enjoy the longer and hotter summers from now on. So what if Lincolnshire disappears. It's a load of crap anyway.

b. Move your deck chair back to avoid getting your feet wet.

c. Rush to the ice cream van and purchase a selection of ice pops, Jublies, Cornettos, Zoom and Fab 21 lollies, and throw them off the end of the pier in a frail attempt to reverse the warming process.

9 Whilst retrieving a football your foot goes through the twelve year old felt roofing on your garden shed. You immediately suspect that this was due to corrosion caused by acid rain. What action would you take?

a. Get a quote for a brand new roof made from a more resistant material such as fuzzy blue asbestos, cyano-acrylate polymer high alumina cement, or something with lead in it.

b. Patch up the hole yourself with a sheet of polythene and some nails.

c. Send a bill for the damage to Environmental Secretary Cecil Parkinson before forming an ad-hoc protest group made up of hippies, teachers, lesbians and people with beards. Then march to Stonehenge to protest about acid rain.

Mr Parkinson yesterday

10 You are visiting friends in the Belgian Congo when you notice a pair of extremely rare monkeys on the brink of extinction. What would you do?

a. Shoot them, stuff their heads and nail them above your fireplace. They'll look great.

b. Attract them by throwing chocolate, gob stoppers and boiled sweets, then take some photos to show your friends after they have become extinct.

*c. Catch them in a big net and open your own zoo. Then make up some boring stories about your family, eat too much, marry a **very nice** American half your age and retire to a convenient tax haven.*

11 You go to the Post Office to cash your giro cheque and notice that the bank notes you receive are not printed on re-cycled paper. How would you respond?

a. Take the cash and spend it on your weekly groceries – high tar cigarettes, beer and pot noodles.

b. Ask for the money to be paid in solid, sturdy, down to earth, ozone friendly ten pence pieces.

c. Take the notes, shred them, pound them in a bucket of water, and make them into solid fuel briquettes by compressing the pulp in a mould and leaving it to dry for six months.

12 You are tending your organic garden when you notice the man in the next allotment attempting to empty a large water filled bath under which you believe several snails may have made their home. You also suspect a couple of frogs might be hibernating in the bath during winter. What action would you therefore take?

a. Give him a hand to tip out the bath and be ready with your shovel to bludgeon any wildlife which may emerge.

b. Take no notice, the frogs are well capable of looking after themselves. And whose bath is it anyway?

David Bellamy – green

c. Stun him with your shovel and chain yourself to the bath, then shout to a friend and ask them to summon David Bellamy or a similar attention seeking celebrity to gain vital publicity and advice.

HOW DID YOU DO?

Award yourself one point for every answer **A**, two points for each **B**, and three points for a **C**.

12 to 19: Disaster! The actions of irresponsible people like yourself threaten the very future of our planet. Unless your attitude to the environment changes drastically, in a few months time the earth will probably wobble off its axis and crash into the sun. Not that you would care.

20 to 29: Room for improvement. Your heart's in the right place. Always remember that our children don't inherit the planet, **we** borrow it from our ancestors and **their** children before them. Try eating more organic lettuce.

30 to 36: Congratulations. You're as green as unripe tomatoes and certain species of melon. You have a mutual love affair with this fragile earth we call our home. You love the trees and the trees love you. Award yourself an extra portion of lentils.

CLUMSY CLAUDE

'MORE LAUGHS WITH THE BUMBLING ANTICS OF THE CLUMSIEST SHITE AROUND'

WUP!

DARNED LOOSE PAVING STONES...

JONESY 1988

ANOTHER HELPING OF UNCO-ORDINATED LUNACY NEXT TIME!

TRIP!

ADVERTISEMENT

LeTTERbOcks o

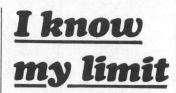

Viz
LETTERBOX
P.O. BOX 1PT
NEWCASTLE UPON TYNE
NE99 1PT

Sick of moaning minnies

Why is it, when old people fall over they make such a song and dance about it, rolling around, moaning, etc? When I fall over, I simply get up, dust my self down and carry on walking. Perhaps these codgers should take a leaf out of my book.

L. Hayman
Birmingham

Whilst on holiday in Holland recently I found these jelly babies on a supermarket shelf.

Mrs V. Pritchard
Ripon

My favourite film is that one with Clint Eastwood when he shoots people with a big gun. He's nails. And the one with the monkey was good too.

P. Aldrich
London

I think blind people shouldn't be allowed to live in country houses, since they can't appreciate the view, and are spoiling the fun for sighted people. In fact, they shouldn't be allowed to have' windows, since it is a complete waste of glass.

G. Elliot
Glasgow

Constabulary criticism inaudibility

Sadly, it seems the trend nowadays is to 'badmouth' the police force, but I won't hear a bad word against them. I've been deaf since birth.

Mrs P. Farnborough
Hants

Why should I pay £66 a year for a television licence? I don't even have a television.

T. Twelvebottoms
Goole
Portsmouth

Last year, my husband and I spent a marvellous week in Bournemouth. This year, we intend to go for a fortnight.

E. Marsden
Leicester

On business in Spain recently, I bought this bottle of lemonade. Can any reader beat that?

Mrs V. Pritchard
Ripon

I live in a small isolated rural community miles from any large town and consequently have never heard of Jonathan Ross, the new Batman film starring Michael Keaton or manned space flight.

Mr F. Brogue
Kirby Malham

Bon Jovi rip-off

At a recent Bon Jovi concert at the NEC, Birmingham, I bought three cans of Vimto, four packets of crisps, four Marathon bars and a packet of polos. I was shocked to be charged a staggering £2.52. The same items could have been bought in my local supermarket for a mere £2.40. It marred my enjoyment of the concert I can tell you.

John Deune
Ely

Whilst on holiday in Crete recently I bought this packet of crisps. Do I win £5?

Mrs V. Pritchard
Ripon

I know my limit

What's all this rubbish talked about drinking and driving. It's all a load of ballyhoo. I regularly drink and drive and have never had an accident (except for one head-on collision in which my wife was paralysed from the neck down.)

Major Percy Reid
Hexborough

When I was a girl, my grandmother used to speak of 'baked potatoes'. Does any reader know what they are and where I could get some from?

Mrs V. Riddel
East Ham

★ Well come on readers, can you help? Maybe you have an old recipe book or perhaps an elderly relative remembers what they are. Perhaps you know other interesting or unusual ways to cook potatoes. Send your suggestions to letterbox, and mark your envelope 'Potato ideas'. There's a crisp tenner for the best suggestion.

The poll tax system is grossly unfair. Why should I have to pay the same amount as my neighbour? I've lived here for 25 years, and he only moved in six months ago.

Scott Groves
Ruddington

I can't slap my wife anymore

What's gone wrong with the world? It seems everyone has gone soft. Nowadays I can't even slap my wife a bit without fear of intervention from the social services or even prosecution.

Major Percy Reid
Hexborough

DOCTOR, I'M NOT A TALL WELL

17"

MW.JW.GPD

GOVERNMENT AXE RINGPIECE TAX

Labour push hard to defeat motion on stool levy

The Government has shelved plans to introduce a new tax on Britain's already beleaguered households.

A new 'toilet tax' bill, similar to a scheme which already operates in Norway, was due to have it's first reading in the House early this year. If passed by Parliament, under the new laws, householders would have to pay an annual charge, in addition to the community charge, proportional to the number of times they used the lavatory.

But now, with the Government losing ground at the polls and facing growing protests against the poll tax, plans to tax us on our toilets have been shelved until after the next election.

FUSS

Tory MP for Fulchester Sunnyoak, Sir Anthony Regents-Park, defended the proposed tax yesterday. "I

Sir Antony Regents-Park – "Sit-down visits".

don't know what all the fuss is about. The system has been long due for an overhaul. And what could possibly be more fair than a system whereby you pay according to how often you use the lavatory?"

RECORD

"There has been a lot of misinformation from the left about this proposed tax", Sir Anthony continued. "And I want to set the record straight. It has never been the Government's intention to tax people every time they use the lavatory. That would be ridiculous and a completely impractical system to operate. What we intend to do is impose a simple, standard charge payable each time a person makes a 'sit-down' visit, so to speak, rather in the same way that your phone bill is calculated".

CASSETTE

But Labour's Derek Twatt slammed the new proposals. "It's an absolute scandal and a disgrace. Under this Tory scheme an elderly, incontinent old lady with an outside lavatory living in Yorkshire could end up paying ten times as much as a rich person living in a castle with twenty toilets, who has complete control over their bowel movements. It's just one more example of the Government robbing the poor to give to the rich".

COMPACT DISC

A senior Government minister last night conceded plans for the toilet tax may have to be reviewed before being presented to Parliament next year. Among possible changes would be the introduction of a rebate for persons medically diagnosed as suffering from diarrhoea, and a standard minimum charge payable by constipated people or people with severely enlarged haemorrhoids.

«TOP TIPS»

AVOID losing contact lenses by drilling a small hole in each and attaching one to the other with a length of fishing line. This is then worn around the neck.
B. Morgan
Criccieth

AVOID bending over to pick up your mail by placing a small table behind the front door.
N. Blackett-Ord
Ashton-u-Lyne

STOP nosey neighbours from knowing which room you are in by stealthily crawling about your house on all fours.
D. E. Blanchard
Fragsthorpe

TRAIL a six foot length of toilet tissue along your bathroom floor, over the rim of your lavatory bowl and into the water. Flush and watch as the paper is 'eaten' like someone sucking spaghetti.
A. Tait
Newcastle

AMAZE your family. Secretly make a pretend candle out of a banana and an almond, then watch their faces as you eat it.
T. Atack
Pontefract

PRETEND you have a fantastic sex life by jumping up and down on your bed and moaning loudly, several times a day. Look at your neighbours' jealous faces each time you leave the house.
P. Pinto
Edgware

MAKE a novel doorbell by threading some tin cans on a piece of string and hang them outside your front door. People can rattle them to attract your attention.
A. Soreskin
Swindon

AVOID being wheel clamped by jacking your car up, removing the wheels and locking them safely in the boot until you return.
Angus Carr
Oxon

NEXT time you have a party make all your guests swallow a small plastic disc with a number on it, making sure to keep a record. If anyone vomits, you'll then know who it was.
Innes Reid
Bangor

KEEP washing up liquid handy by storing it in the kitchen. I keep mine in a cupboard under the sink.
L. Bowman
Tulsa

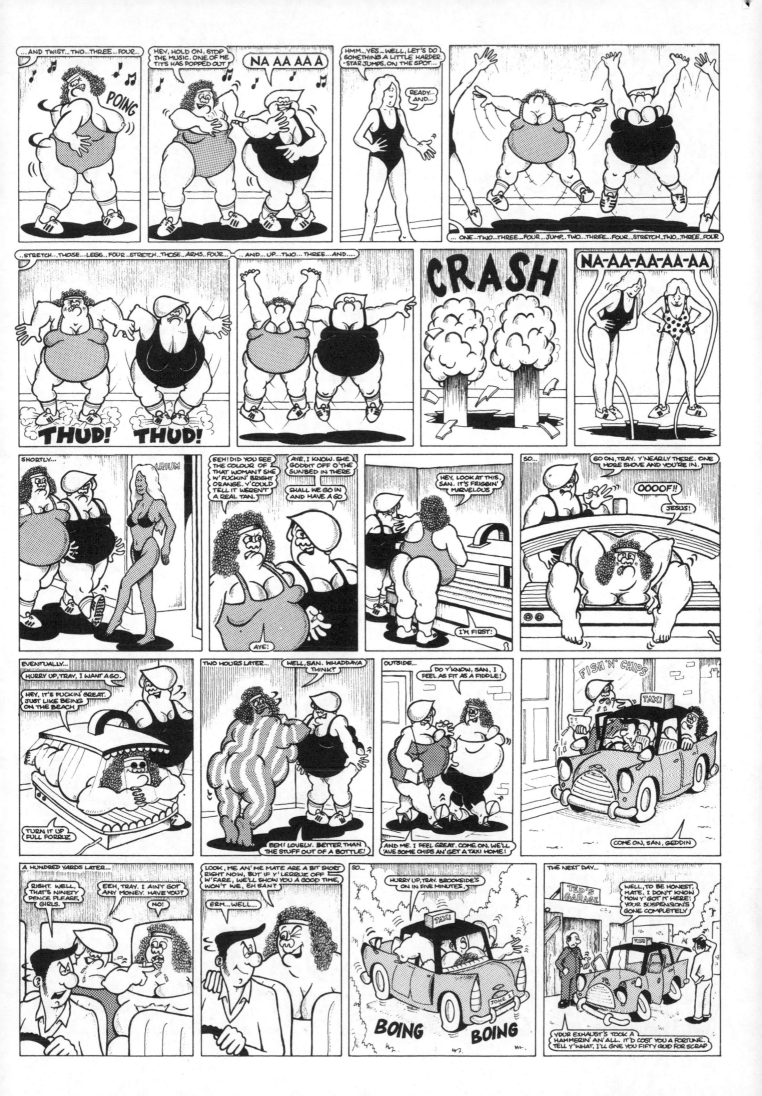

95

96

20 THINGS YOU NEVER KNEW ABOUT RUSSIA

A little over a year ago no-one had even heard of Russia. For all we knew it was just another country somewhere in Europe. But now communist leader Michael Gorbachev has put Russia firmly on the map. It's in the papers and on the telly, and in pubs and clubs all over Britain people are talking about little else.

Love it or hate it, nowadays you simply can't ignore Russia. But what is it *really* like? Here are a few things you probably didn't know about the USSR.

1 Russia is by far and away the biggest country in the world. Except for Canada.

2 Despite it's enormous size Russian has a relatively small population, roughly equivalent to that of Wales.

3 Russia is famous for it's spies. Some famous names rumoured to have been Russian spies include Roger Hollis, former head of MI5, ex-Prime Minister Harold Wilson and children's TV presenter and newsreader John Craven.

4 Not all Russians are spies. There are Russian doctors, electricians, gas fitters and even landscape gardeners. In fact, almost half the population of Russia have no connection whatsoever with the KGB.

5 In Russia the staple diet consists of potato. To stay alive the average Russian has to eat *three times* his body weight in potatoes – every week!

6 Russian shoppers queue for hours to buy bread, which is in short supply, while caviar is given away free on street corners. That's because sturgeon, the plant that caviar comes from, grows wild in Russia where it is generally regarded as a weed.

'Pauls' of Moscow, The world's first barbers shop, opened in 1923.

7 Russia invented the barber's shop. The first ever gentleman's hairdressers was opened in a Moscow side street in 1923.

8 Russian leader Michael Gorbachev likes nothing better in his spare time than listening to western pop music. His favourite groups include Five Star and Sister Sledge.

9 Alcoholism is a serious problem in Russia with 8 out of 10 Russians registered as alcoholics. However, the Moscow branch of Alcoholics Anonymous has only one phone line, which is constantly engaged.

10 Russia is made up of many republics, the smallest of which is Ludbanskia with a population of only 4.

11 Visit the USSR for a holiday and you will immediately notice that unlike other countries Russia has no tourist attractions. After the communist revolution in 1914, all tourist attractions were demolished, and sandy beaches around the Russian coastline were covered over with rubble.

12 Russia's best known actor is Walter Koenig who played 'Chekov' in the hit TV series Star Trek. Relatively unknown in the United States, Koenig enjoys megastar status in his native country where his acting career has made him Russia's wealthiest man, owning six pairs of shoes. He has also become a pop star, topping the soviet pops for an incredible 6 years with his version of the Shirley Bassey hit 'Hey Big Spender'.

Walter Koenig's record breaking single spent 6 years at No. 1, selling over 300 copies.

13 Russia is the flattest country in the world. Its highest mountain, Mount Bonsnov, is only 47 feet high.

14 Britain and Germany weren't the only two countries involved in the second world war. Russia also took part, coming third behind us and America.

15 With 17 different indiginous species, Russia has more types of mouse than any other country in the world.

16 Despite having no fewer than 149 letters in their alphabet, there is no world for 'tooth' in the Russian language.

Mikhail Gorbachev – Sister Sledge.

17 Russian families spend their evenings huddled around the TV set – watching British programmes! For the top rated TV show in the USSR is 'Catchphrase', hosted by silver haired comic Roy Walker. However, viewing figures can be misleading. For in Russia there are only 3 television sets. Two belong to Walter Koenig, and the other one is broken.

18 It's no wonder the Russian's make good spies. They have the best eyesight in the world! Only 1 in 500 Russians wear spectacles. And it's just as well. You'd have to queue for 2 weeks to have your eyes tested at a Moscow opticians, and a pair of glasses with just basic frames would cost over a million rubles — that's £800 to you and me – the equivalent of three years wages to the average Russian!

19 A second-hand pair of Levi 501 jeans, originally bought for £24.99 in a London boutique, were recently sold at an auction in Moscow for a staggering £23 million. The buyer – Walter Koenig.

20 Tipton in the West Midlands has close links with Russia. In 1982 it was twinned with the Russian city of Kiev. Every Easter the mayor of Kiev sends his West Midlands counterpart a large oven-ready chicken stuffed with garlic and butter.

HAVE-A-GO HERO FRANK TEACHES THUGS LESSON

Hero Frank nursing bruised knuckles yesterday.

Have-a-go hero Frank Barker wasn't prepared to stand back and watch the day heartless youths raided his back garden to steal apples.

Frank, a plucky 38 year old, sprang into action and challenged the would-be thieves. One of the gang fled empty handed, while Frank grappled with the other two.

COLLAR

"I managed to get hold of one of them by the collar and punch him in the eye", said Frank, who was recovering from the incident at home yesterday. "I then managed to pull him to the ground and kicked him several times".

"The next thing I knew out of the corner of my eye I caught a glimpse of the other one running for the gate". Frank was having none of it. "I instinctively grabbed a short length of rusty drainpipe which had been lying on the ground and caught him on the back of the head with it".

CUFFS

Fourteen stone Frank, a keen boxer during his army days, then managed to rain a series of heavy blows down on the thugs until a neighbour, alerted by their screams, raised the alarm. The police arrived and the intruders, aged 11 and 12 years, were carted off to hospital for emergency treatment.

"At the time I wasn't scared", said brave Frank, who was nursing bruised knuckles suffered in the attack. "I didn't really think about it. Looking back I suppose it was a pretty foolhardy thing to do, but you have to stand up for yourself and defend your property. Especially nowadays".

PADDED SHOULDERS

Fulchester's Neighbourhood Watch organiser Glenda Purvis was first to congratulate Frank. "He's a very brave man and we're all very proud of him". Local Bobby P.C. Alan Jones agreed, but added a note of caution. "If you see anything suspicious, call the police. Our advice to the public is not to approach criminals. You'll be far safer leaving that to us".

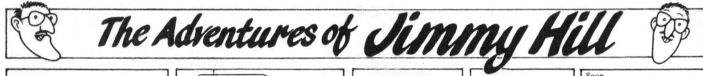

CURSED!

Tragedy stalks the cast of favourite TV show

A catalogue of tragedy has befallen the cast of one of Britain's favourite TV shows. And it has lead to claims that there is a **CURSE** on the popular TV comedy series Dad's Army.

For ten years actor JOHN LAURIE played eerie undertaker Fraser in the series. In 1985 he attended one final funeral – his own.

In 1987 the acting world was shocked by the death of JOHN LE MESURIER. He was 75. He had brilliantly portrayed the platoon's mild mannered Sergeant Wilson.

Tragedy struck again when Le Mesurier's former wife, fellow actress HATTIE JACQUES, also died.

Jacques' on-screen brother ERIC SYKES has himself fallen foul of the curse. He suffers from a perforated eardrum.

For no fewer than **SIX** of the stars have died tragically in recent years.

TRAGIC

Based upon the adventures of a bungling platoon of Britain's Home Guard during the second world war, Dad's Army has constantly topped the viewing figures with regular audiences of over 17 million. But success has now been overshadowed by a tragic series of events which have befallen the cast, crew and even the programme writers.

DEATH

Everyone connected with the series was shocked and saddened by the death of actor James Beck in 1973. He had been well known for his portrayal of cocky Private Walker. But it became a double tragedy when shortly afterwards, in 1977, Edward Sinclair who played the verger Mr. Yeatman, died after an intermittent illness.

BAD LUCK

Over the following ten years no fewer than FOUR more members of the cast were to die in what, on the face of it, were unconnected incidents. Arthur Lowe, Arnold Ridley, John Laurie and John Le Mesurier all having passed away. And bad luck has befallen many surviving members of the cast.

INJURED

Clive Dunn, famous for his catch phrase "Don't panic!" suffered a minor accident while gardening, and has since retired to Portugal. Ian Lavender, the youngest member of the cast, injured a thumb while installing central heating pipes at his home. No longer the fresh faced "stupid boy" he portrayed as Private Pike, time has taken its toll on grey haired Lavender who has not always found acting work easy to find.

ROLL CALL OF DOOM

Of these smiling faces only five remain alive today. (Back row, left to right) John Laurie (died 1985), writer Jim Perry, Arnold Ridley (died at his home in Norwood, Middlesex, 1984, aged 88), Bill Pertwee as Warden Hodges, James Beck (died 1973), writer David Croft, Ian Lavender. (Front row, kneeling) John Le Mesurier (died 1987), Arthur 'Captain Mainwaring' Lowe (dropped dead in his dressing room at Birmingham's Alexandra theatre, 1983) and Clive Dunn who, after recording the hit record 'Grandad' fled to Portugal to start a new life.

It is not only the actors in the jinxed series who have suffered. One BBC lighting technician, who preferred to remain anonymous, spoke of nightmarish technical breakdowns and hitches that haunted the show throughout its 11 year history.

SUFFERED

"On one occasion an electric generator we were using broke down and it took us two hours to find a replacement. And on another occasion a van being used to transport costumes suffered a flat tyre. No sooner than we'd fixed it, the fan belt broke".

DISASTERS

Many insiders are convinced that it was disasters like these which eventually led to the programme being taken off the air in 1977. But despite the fact that its run ended 13 years ago, Dad's Army is still proving to be as unlucky as ever.

DAMAGE

"During the recent repeats of the series a continuity announcer who was possibly due to introduce the programme the following week was involved in a car crash. Although he wasn't injured, his car suffered considerable damage", our source revealed.

TRAGEDIES

Since creating the hit series, writers Jimmy Perry and David Croft have also been involved in a string of tragedies. These have included "It ain't 'alf hot mum', 'Are you being served?' and 'Hi-De-Hi'.

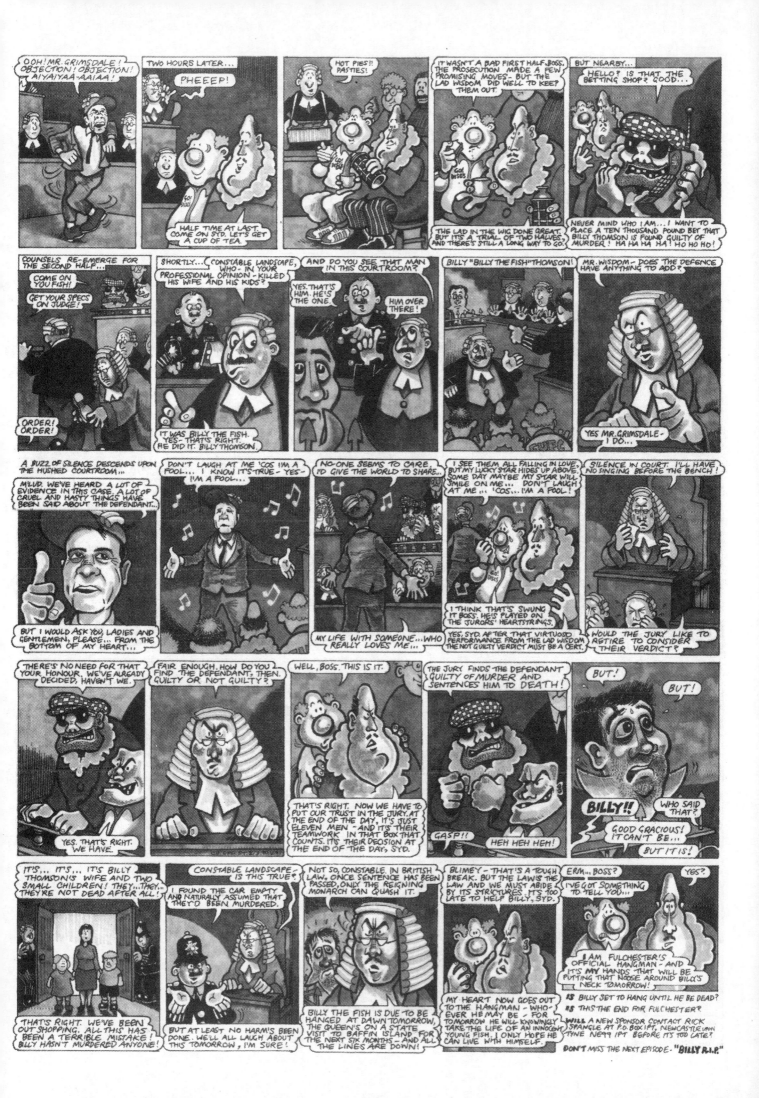

103

106

POSSESSED!

A terrified Glasgow father has issued a desperate plea for help. "Please help me save my son. He is the Devil incarnate".

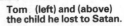
EXCLUSIVE

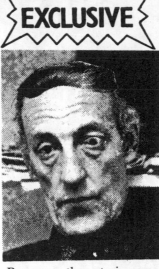

Tom (left) and (above) the child he lost to Satan.

Satan stalks the Earth ~in my son's body

Ever since his son Damien was born 14 years ago, Tom McAllister has lead a one man campaign to have him exorcised, a campaign that has cost Tom his home, his marriage and eventually his liberty. But Tom remains convinced that Satan has come to Earth in his son's body.

NIGHTMARE

"These last 14 years have been like a nightmare from which there is no awakening", Tom told us. "I have fought a battle with the forces of evil, and through the eyes of my son I have come face to face with Satan himself".

IT

When Damien was born he was given a clean bill of health by staff at the local maternity hospital, and Tom's wife Margaret was allowed to take the baby home after 4 days. "We were the happiest couple in the world", Tom recalls, "but then it started to happen".

EVIL

Tom's face turns white as he recalls how the first signs of evil began to manifest themselves. "The day we got back from the hospital I was sitting holding the baby. Margaret was in the kitchen. Suddenly I felt a jolt through Damien's body, and I looked down to see sick spurting out of his mouth. Then he just looked at me. I could sense great evil. It was frightening".

SCREAMS

The vomiting continued, especially after feeds. "At times he would wake during the night, vomit, then we'd hear chilling screams from his cot. I would try picking him up, but the screaming would continue. Then he'd stop, suddenly, and just look at me. It was then that I first sensed Satan within him, and that my son was possessed by the Devil".

Tom explained his concerns to wife Margaret, but she was sceptical, despite increasing evidence which by now included brightly coloured excrement. "One day I was changing his nappy. The Devil obviously though I was trying to exorcise his spirit, so Damien was screaming wildly. Suddenly I noticed the mess in his nappy was bright green, just like the sick in that film 'The Omen'. I pointed this out to the health visitor, but she said it was normal. At this point I first suspected that something was wrong. I knew this was the work of Beelzebub. Damien was not my son. He was the son of Satan – the Devil incarnate."

EXORCISM

Tom contacted a local priest. "I knew the only way I could save him was by exorcism, but the priest didn't seem interested. He suggested we have him christened instead."

LUCIFER

As Tom left the church, he felt an evil presence watching over him. "Branches in nearby trees began to sway slightly in the wind, and it seemed to get a bit darker. I realised then, for the first time, that I was engaged in mortal combat with Lucifer himself, and the battle had only just begun".

By now the strain was beginning to show on Tom's marriage. Margaret had been unhappy with Tom's choice of name, and she objected to sprigs of parsley that he had nailed to his son's bedroom door. She even called the police after finding the figures '666' scrawled on the baby's head with what appeared to be a felt pen. But Tom denies her accusations. "That birth mark was just another sign, another sign which Margaret chose to ignore".

HOSPITAL

Margaret successfully obtained a court order banning Tom from their council flat. After a short spell in police custody, Tom was sent to a hospital for psychiatric reports and didn't see his son again for almost a year.

MIRACLE

"I went to visit Margaret on Damien's first birthday. I took along a couple of toys for him. He seemed to be much better, and I thought for a moment that a miracle had occurred, that he was saved.

HORRIFIC

Then suddenly he began hurling the toys around the room with what seemed like inhuman strength. One, a solidly built Tonka truck, was broken. Then he stopped, looked up towards me, and uttered a work in an horrific deep voice. He said 'mama', or something like that, but I immediately recognised this as the voice of Satan".

CANDELABRA

That evening Tom was arrested trying to break into the flat carrying several wooden stakes, a candelabra and a mallet. "I was trying to save my son, not harm him", Tom insists. But after further tests he was returned to long-term psychiatric care.

CRUET

After several unsuccessful escape attempts, Tom now spends his time praying for his son behind the bars of a high security mental institution in Arbroath. But he has these words of warning for his wife Margaret and others who have scoffed at his claims.

GRAVY BOAT

"I believe this is just the beginning. The dawn of the beginning of the end. Damien was sporned of the Devil, son of Satan, to bring about Armagedon. Evil shall conquer Good. The seas will boil, the earth open up and all mankind shall be swallowed. There will be death, disease, and eternal suffering for all of us for evermore. And it will be the end of the world. You mark my words."

NAPKIN RINGS

Tom claims his fears have been confirmed by a series of tragedies which have affected his family since his son's birth. Several of Tom's aunts have died, a nephew was badly injured in a car crash, and in October 1986 a tree fell on a car belonging to Margaret's sister Elaine. Luckily no-one was hurt.

111

SEX FOR SALE!

Sex is for sale on the streets of Britain, often for as little as £5.

Our investigation into widespread prostitution has revealed a dramatic increase in the amount of sex available for money. And as a result of rising mortgage rates and the poll tax, more and more hard-up housewives are going 'on the game' in order to make ends meet.

For many hard pressed households the only answer to rising bills is to turn on the red light and offer sexual services for cash. And if the money is right, customers can have anything they want.

SCANDAL

We sent investigators onto the streets to uncover the scandal of Britain's booming brothels. After hearing reports of suspicious goings on at a house in the quiet village of Little Barton, we rang up the owner, a Mrs. Wilson, and arranged to visit her that afternoon.

HAIRED

Mrs. Wilson, a small, grey-haired lady in her fifties met us at the door and we were ushered inside. "What exactly is it that you want?" she asked.

MESS

Dirty dishes littered a small coffee table and several newspapers were scattered around the floor. "I'm afraid

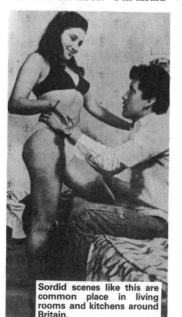
Sordid scenes like this are common place in living rooms and kitchens around Britain.

Investigators blow lid off housewives sex scandal

this place is a bit of a mess", she explained, "but I can offer you a cup of tea". But when our investigators mentioned sex, Mrs. Wilson's tone changed completely.

FULL SEX

"I think you'd better leave", she snapped. We then offered Mrs. Wilson £40 for full sex, at which point she began to ring the police. Our investigators made their excuses and left.

REVEALING

Neighbours in the picturesque village of Bradbury had no idea what the attractive, middle aged lady who had recently moved into No. 3 Church Cottages did for a living. Adverts placed in the local press said merely 'Piano Tuition' followed by a telephone number. We rang the number and arranged an 'appointment' for early the next morning. When our investigators called the door was answered by a woman dressed in a revealing blouse and slippers. She introduced herself simply as 'Mrs. Murray'.

FRUIT

Our man was led to a small room at the back of the house. Shelves were strewen with plates, cups and a bowl containing several large pieces of fruit. In the centre of the room was a large piano.

BEGINNER

"It's ten pounds an hour", our investigator was told. "Have you done it before, or are you just a beginner?" Mrs. Murray was quite happy to talk about her work. "I do it for the money", she admitted. "Shall we

Another sordid scene similar to the one shown below, left.

get started then?" At this point our investigator made his excuses and left.

PROSTITUTES

The brightly lit alleyways and escalators of London's Underground act as a vast sex supermarket where perverts and prostitutes meet and do business in a 24-hour roundabout merry-go-round of non-stop sex for sale.

It's behind doors similar to this one that sordid scenes (like those pictured above and bottom left) take place.

At Kings Cross tube station a young girl stood by a coin operated vending machine. "How much is it?" our investigator asked, waving a bunch of notes discreetly. "It only takes ten pence pieces, and I think it's jammed", the young girl replied.

POSITIONS

Girls like this, many as young as 15 and 16, can be found on every railway platform in Britain. "Can you change a fifty pence piece?" our investigator was asked. At this point he made his excuses and left.

Stall holders at a street market in Camden, North London, regularly offer sexual services over the counter. At one fruit stall a subtle menu of sex was on clear view. Round firm melons were displayed alongside ripe bananas. Nearby there was a box of plums.

GRAPEFRUIT

Our reporter approached the stall holder, a man in his early thirties, and pretended to be interested in a grapefruit. "Grapefruits are 26p each", he was told. Our man then pointed towards his trousers and asked whether sex was available.

ORAL

The stallholder disappeared briefly before returning with another man. Our investigator was then lead to nearby waste ground, punched in the face and kicked several times about the head and body, before he made his excuses and left.

LETTERBOCKS

These vicars make me sick

Vicars have it easy. They don't pay tax, they get a free house, they only work one day a week and then they have the cheek to pass the plate round on a Sunday looking for tips.

It's about time Mrs Thatcher hit the vicars where it hurts – in the pocket. I say *treble* the poll tax for vicars and make them pay an extra £1 per foot of steeple on their church. Why should Joe Muggins have to pay extra in order to subsidise these men who wear skirts, drink tea all day and talk twaddle for 15 minutes every Sunday morning.

Mr T Evans
Somerset

What a con most of these so-called 'calendars' are. Not so the superb effort from Viz, which gives us a whopping 31 days in April, instead of the paltry 30 on offer from all the others.

What a bargain for my fiver! Leap year value, in a month when it's warm enough to enjoy the extra day.

A Scrattock
Cirencester

The other day whilst playing Scrabble with my wife I started and was able to make the word 'RESTORE' using all of my seven letters. I got a double word score, however my wife went on to win the game.

T More
Hampton

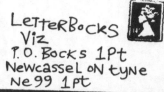

LetterBocks
Viz
P.O. Bocks 1Pt
Newcassel on Tyne
Ne99 1Pt

Do any of your readers know anyone who might want a giant panda cub? I have two giant pandas which I keep as pets and they breed like nobody's business. I've already had to drown 40 cubs since Christmas.

Mr D Bentley
Birmingham

Anyone fancy a fight?

I think I'm a pretty hard case and I like to put myself around a bit. Would any of your readers like to have a fight?

C Goldson
Hampshire

As a parent I am disgusted by the ever increasing price of children's toys. In our day we made our own entertainment – by playing with a stick and a ball of string.

Dick Price
Walthamstow

HOW LONG HAS YOUR HOUSE BEEN ON THE MARKET BRIAN?

As a vicar, I can sympathise with Mr Evans' remarks (Letterbox, Viz 42). I appreciate that many people are struggling to make ends meet especially since the introduction of the community charge. Whilst it is true that vicars only work one day out of seven, Mr Evans has obviously overlooked the fact that we are also required to work on Christmas Day (for no extra pay) while everyone else is at home watching TV and opening their presents.

He would do well to get his facts right next time.

Rev A Marshall
Crantock

What about me? I am a Jewish vicar, and as well as working the same hours as other vicars I have to wear a silly hat, a long beard and am not allowed to eat sausages. *And* I don't get any presents at Christmas.

My life already. These English vicars don't know they're born.

Rabbi B Goldstein
Mousehole

*Are you a vicar? If so, are you overworked or do you have it easy? Come on, you Holy men. There's a dozen candles for the best letter we receive. Write to our usual letterbox address, and mark your envelopes 'Vicars Debate'.

'Thank you' to the motorist who flashed his headlights and allowed me to pull out into a busy street the other day. If it had not been for him I may well have arrived at the shops a few minutes later than I had planned.

Mr R Ellis
Stroud

How about a picture of a bloke kissing that bird's arse?

Tom McArthur
Bolton

*Here you are Tom. Happy to oblige.

Whilst having sex have any of your readers tried pushing a drawing pin into their buttocks and knocking it home with a heavy book?

If so, I should like to know what it's like, as my wife and I have yet to try it.

Major B Bradshaw
Aldershot

TOP TIPS

PREVENT eggs from rolling off kitchen work surfaces by keeping them in a small bowl or similar receptacle.

L Bowman
Tijuana

ENTERTAIN your family with a comical impression of snooker star Dennis Taylor by simply wearing your glasses upside down.

B Potter
Aberdeen

IF a dog is about to attack you in the street, stand your ground. Do not show any signs of fear as this will encourage the animal to attack.

Mrs B Sellers
Cricklewood

TEACH your children the value of money by bursting their football. They will then have to *work* to earn enough to buy a replacement.

Mr G Moran
Finchley

DOLLY MIXTURE PIC N' MIX
B AHRAM LEATHER GOODS
FAMILY BUTCHER
SMITH GENERAL HARDWARE

114

YES, WE HAVE NO BANANAS

That was the shock message from greengrocers up and down the country as supplies of our favourite fruit began drying up yesterday.

There were scenes reminiscent of World War Two rationing as housewives queued to snap up the few bananas that remained on Britain's supermarket shelves. And electricity chiefs reported a sudden drop in demand for electricity as people switched off their kettles and went out in search of bananas.

Shell shocked shopkeepers blame the shortage on greedy growers in Africa who are **CHOPPING DOWN** banana trees and **CASHING IN** on increased demand for turnips, swedes and radishes.

"As a result of the Chernobyl disaster Eastern Europe's vegetable crop has consistently failed," explains Dr Wolfgang Zimmerman, lecturer in Fruit and Vegetables at Loughborough University. And prices on the world vegetable market have reached record levels as farmhouse soup manufacturers attempt to out bid each other for the limited supplies which are available.

Greenpeace believe that one thousand square miles of African banana forest is being felled *every fifteen minutes* to make way for vegetables. "People don't realise that the African banana forests are a major source of oxygen, and bananas," a spokesman told us. "If we continue to destroy them at this rate we could all suffocate by the year 2000."

A spokesman for the International Federation of Farmhouse and Country Vegetable Soup Manufacturers denied this claim. "People would be just as quick to complain if there was no turnips, swedes or radishes in their soup," he told us. "There are two sides to every coin."

Meanwhile black marketeers are enjoying a field day. One man we spoke to at King's Cross station offered to sell us a banana for £200. "I've got three. You can have them all for five hundred," he told us.

WHEN under attack from a large polar bear, roll into a ball and remain perfectly still. Any movement on your part will excite the animal and increase your chance of injury.

Mrs B Sellers
Cricklewood

BEAT the credit card companies at their own game. Run up a massive bill on your credit cards and then kill yourself before your statement arrives, thus avoiding re-payment.

D Payne
Middlesex

IF being pursued by a rogue rhinoceros, run in a straight line directly away from the animal. Just before he catches you, dart quickly to one side or another. Unable to change direction, the bulky animal's momentum will carry him a good distance away, enabling you to run up a tree and call for help.

Mrs B Sellers
Cricklewood

RE-SPRAYING your car? Cover it with 'cling-film' first. If you don't like the new colour simply peel it off and start again with another.

Denise Jordan
Petts Wood

DON'T panic when being chased over land by a crocodile. Simply run in a zig-zag fashion. These large reptiles are only able to run in straight lines and will be confused by your constant changes of direction and will soon give up the chase.

Mrs B Sellers
Cricklewood

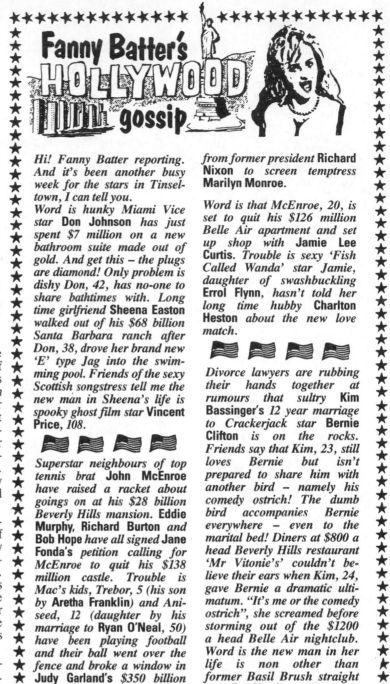

SCARGILL IN NAZI SPACE GUN HORROR

The National Union of Mineworkers have denied allegations that several million pounds collected during the 1984 miners' strike were used by their chairman Arthur Scargill to build a 1,000 foot long steel tubular artillary gun at his home near Barnsley.

PINKO

Commie union boss Scargill, 54, has so far failed to comment on the further allegation that he paid former Nazi war criminals 75p an hour to act as his personal 'minders' during the fourteen month long dispute.

M.O.D. experts believe that the alleged gun, if it existed, which it didn't, could fire big things a very long way. Perhaps even into space.

116

MY LIFE WITH T

"**Jagger, Bowie, Fish out of Marillion. You name 'em, I've fitted their kitchens. And some of the stories I could tell you, you just wouldn't believe.**

One day I had an appointment to measure up for a new kitchen at Rod Stewart's Surrey mansion. He was living with stunning film star Britt Ekland at the time, and I remember arriving to find some sort of sex and drugs orgy in full swing. There were naked women, most of them top celebrities, in every room. Champagne was flowing like confetti.

SEX

Anyway, I made my way to the kitchen and couldn't believe what I saw. It was narrow – about 7 feet wide by 13½ long, with only one outside wall. I immediately realised a peninsula work unit was out of the question. The choice of position of the cooker was also limited. Rod's idea of a ranch style breakfast .bar was a nonstarter.

SEXY BRITT

I measured up as best I could, then went to find Rod to tell him the score. I found him upstairs on a bed having sex with some film star, so I told Britt I'd pop a quote in the post within a day or two.

VIBRATOR

A fortnight later the job was mine. Rod took my advice and plumped for a straight galley design with a built-in electric hob and matching eye-level cupboards, all finished in grey melamine with marble effect work surfaces and extruded aluminium trim. The whole lot came to £400 – a lot of money in those days – but Rod was very happy with the job.

SEXY ROD

Choosing your kitchen is probably the hardest decision you ever have to make — even for the stars. One day I got a call from Mick Jagger. Could I come over immediately and fit a kitchen. I threw a few tools in the van and headed straight for Mick's Surrey mansion.

SPANKED

It wasn't long after Brian Jones had died, and the band were all sat around writing songs and taking drugs. I went straight through to the kitchen which was a large basement room at the back of the house. Mick had indicated a preference for a traditional country kitchen in solid pine and left the finer details up to Mariane Faithful. After all, she was going to be the one doing the cooking.

SEXY MARIANE

I'd heard a lot about Mariane, especially in the tabloid papers. In those days she had quite a reputation, but even so I was surprised by her choice of part

Most of us never get to meet our pop idols. But for a lucky few – technicians, roadies, sound and light engineers – mixing with the stars is just a part of their job. And one man, RONNIE ROBINSON, has perhaps got closer to the stars than anyone throughout his 25 year career as a kitchen fitter, fitting kitchens for all of the biggest names in the music world.

'The drugs, the booze, the naked sex orgies ~ I've seen it all'

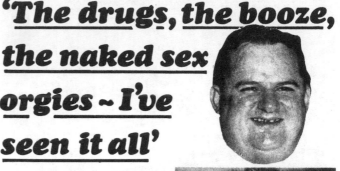

glazed green and white alternating tiles for the splash back. I would have to order them specially from the warehouse and it could take up to 14 days for delivery. But she was adamant, so I placed the order and got on with the rest of the work.

BREASTS

When the tiles arrived I had everything else finished so all that remained was to put them up. Simple, I thought. Little did I know the splashback height didn't coincide with the size of the tiles, and I was there all afternoon trimming the top row to size.

TONGUE

Anyway, I'd just finished grouting the last tile when in walks Mick, not with Mariane, but with Bianca Jagger, the new girl in his life. She took one look at the tiles and shook her head. "I want those removed", she said. Mick was so embarrassed, but I'm a pro, so I just got on with the job, replacing the tiles with self-adhesive 'tile-on-a-role' wall covering – the wipe clean type. It looks good, but lasts nothing like as long as a good ceramic surface.

NAKED

When I was finished I sealed the work surface edging with a half inch quadrant ramin and cellulose varnish. I was glad to see the back of that kitchen, I can tell you.

GEORGE HARRISON

Several years later a good friend of mine, George Harrison, invited me to a party at his Surrey mansion where I met Mick. Believe it or not his new lover Jerry Hall had decided she hated vinyl wall covering and wanted it replaced – wait for it – with the original green and white tiles! Luckily I'd removed them all carefully and stacked them in my shed. After a quick polish they looked as good as new, and I stuck them up the next day.

ERECT NIPPLES

You wouldn't believe the way some pop stars carry on. They spend a fortune on cars, parties, booze and drugs, but when it comes to investing a few bob in a decent quality fitted kitchen some of them simply don't want to know.

ORGASM

I was having a drink with Radio One DJ Simon Bates one evening. The previous night he'd done Top Of The

E STARS

SEXY SIMES

LEMMY (out of Motorhead)

Pops, and between takes Lemmy, out of Motorhead, had told Simes he was having trouble with his kitchen. By coincidence I was just finishing a job at Freddie Mercury's so the next day I popped in to see Lemmy, who lives just round the corner.

THROBBED

Lemmy told me that smoke was building up in his kitchen whenever he used the deep fat fryer, and as a result his suspended polystyrene ceiling tiles were filthy. A quick inspection revealed that the extractor hood on his Tricity 7 flush mounted hob wasn't working – the filters were clogged up.

THRUST

I gave Lemmy a price to overhaul the hood and replace the filters – a ballpark figure of between fifty and sixty quid. His reply was unprintable. Instead, he asked me to remove the filters and then simply replace the cowling on the hood. In return he said he'd buy me a drink. I explained that such a move would leave live wires exposed to temperatures in excess of the manufacturer's recognised safety perameters. As a responsible member of the National Guild of Kitchen Fitters, I had no choice but to pick up my tools and leave.

MOAN

If I had carried out that work, I would not only have been risking my professional reputation as a kitchen fitter, but also the lives of Lemmy out of Motorhead and his family. That was

something I was not prepared to do. I later heard from Mark Knopfler that Lemmy was cooking again, and using his hood without filters. Although I'm not prepared to name names, I know who carried out this work. Lemmy out of Motorhead's kitchen is now a powder keg, just waiting to explode. The fitter concerned could have that on his conscience for the rest of his life.

SEXY

Luckily not all pop stars have the same scant regard for kitchen safety regulations. The vast majority play it strictly by the rules. Take my mate Phil Collins. I've lost count of the number of kitchens I've put in for Phil over the years. It could be two or maybe three. But every time he tells me, 'Ronnie. Safety first, I don't care what it costs.' I wish all my customers were like Phil".

You can delve deeper into the secret lives of the stars by reading Ronnie's new book 'I FITTED LOADS OF STARS' KITCHENS' by Ronnie Robinson (Turnip Books, £13.95), available from most good book shops, and W. H. Smiths.

HE WANTED FIFTY QUID FOR THE WARDROBE BUT I MANAGED TO KNOCK HIM DOWN

121

I WAS THIRD KRAY TWIN

A man claiming to be the 'third Kray twin' yesterday issued a cocky challenge to the British police from his new home on the Costa del Crime. "Having a lovely time — wish you were here!"

Kevin Kray, 27, claims he was the brains behind the Kray's notorious gangland empire in the 60's. And when his twin brothers Ronnie and Reggie were jailed for life in 1969 Kevin fled to Spain, taking with him most of the proceeds from their Mafia-style Eastend operation.

CASE

"I knew the old bill were on my case, so I quit while I was ahead". And while his brothers begin their twenty-first year behind bars, Kevin lives a life of luxury in his £1,200 caravan on a campsite near Malaga.

HANDBAG

"They say crime doesn't pay. Well, I know different", says Kevin, cracking open another can of lager before sitting back to reflect on his life of crime.

HOLDALL

"I remember the sixties well. No-one messed with the Krays. Me and my brothers had London all sewn up. We'd get up in the morning, and rob a bank or two before breakfast. Then in the evening we'd go and murder someone in a pub. It was a great life I can tell you".

SHOPPING TROLLEY

"I knew all the villains. Buster Keaton, Ronnie Knight, John McVicar and Ronald Biggs. In fact, it was me who told old Ronnie Biggs to do the great train robbery – that was *my* idea".

IGNORED

Kevin is understandably annoyed that his part in the Kray's story has been totally ignored by the makers of the hit film 'The Krays', starring the Kemp brothers out of Spandau Ballet. And despite his wealth and luxury lifestyle, Kevin is up in arms about payments being made to his brothers by the makers of the film.

The Kray twins in their heyday (below) Kevin, Reggie and Ronnie, and (left) Kevin today, living it up on the Costa del Crime.

"It's not fair. Ronnie and Reggie always got all the credit, and now they're getting the money from the film. But I was the mastermind behind our Eastend operations. And I was always meaner than them. Come to think of it, I shot more people in pubs than both of them put together".

REPUTATION

Kevin is quick to point out that despite their reputation for violence, the Krays always played fair. "There were strict rules. We didn't just kill anyone – we only shot our own. And coppers. But that was the way in the Eastend. We were one big happy family".

FORGET

"I'll never forget those days. And my old mum, Scarlet. She was fantastic. Just like Lou Beale out of Eastenders".

WRITE

Kevin plans to write his own film version of the Kray's story, starring Neil Tennant out of the Pet Shop Boys as himself. "I don't need the money – I'm probably a millionaire several times over – but I think it's time the true story was told", he explained.

LEFT

Production rights to his film are available for £500 (or nearest offer) from Kevin who can be contacted at his caravan, 'Poloma Blanca', Bel Vista Park, Campo Del Sol, Malaga, Spain.

IT'S A DOG'S LIFE!
Hot under collar Terry's in the doghouse

Terry Thompson thought he'd seen the last of his dog Candy when the loveable labrador went missing during a camping holiday in Cornwall in 1971.

After all attempts to find the dog had failed, eleven year old Terry was in tears as he reluctantly returned to his home in Solihull.

CANDY

Terry had given up all hope of ever seeing Candy alive again. That was until one day in January of this year when Terry, now 30, opened his door to find Candy sitting on the step.

SODA POP

"I couldn't believe it after all those years Candy had somehow managed to find her way home." Despite the dog's nineteen year ordeal Candy was in good health. "She was a lot smaller than before, and a slightly different colour, and breed, but I'd recognise that wagging tail anywhere."

SASPERILLA

But Terry's joy soon turned to anger when next door neighbour Barry Jenkins rang his doorbell claiming the dog was *his* pet Rex, and had strayed into Terry's garden through a gap in the fence.

A heated argument ensued and Terry was subsequently arrested and charged with assault, threatening behaviour, and stealing a dog.

POTATO CHIPS

Despite being found guilty and fined £45 Terry remains adamant that the dog is his. "I won't rest until Candy is back where she belongs," he told us yesterday. "And if I don't get her back I'm going to put that bastard's windows in."

OOH! IT MAKES ME SO MAD. SOMEONE'S BEEN SQUEEZING THE TOOTHPASTE FROM THE MIDDLE OF THE TUBE AGAIN. AND PUTTING THE USED MATCHES BACK IN THE BOX...

I'M ARRESTING YOU FOR BEING A PETTY THIEF.

BONKING ON THE BUSES!

Fellas. What's **YOUR** idea of the most glamourous job in the world? Film star, stunt rider or international spy perhaps? It's certainly true that men in these professions pull their fair share of gorgeous girls.

James Bond for example has sex with up to four girls in each film, while Eddie Kidd is never seen with the same top model twice. But bus driver **LES TAYLOR** claims these occupations are a bore compared to bus driving. According to Les all the action takes place on the buses!

In his new book 'Sex On The Buses' Les blows the lid off Britain's bonking bus drivers. They're all at it, according to Les. Here, in an exclusive extract from his book, Les lets us in on just some of the sexational secrets of life behind the wheel.

Lusty Les drives the girls wild 'I always give them a good ride'

Les (left) and a bus.

' A lot of people imagine its boring driving a bus back and forth along the same route every day. But nothing could be further from the truth.

My favourite route ran through a housing estate. it was the number 47, but back at the depot we called it the '69' for obvious reasons. I'd take my bus down there at 9.30 after all the fellas had gone to work, and the birds would be *queuing up for it* at every stop. I'd make sure every one of them got *a good ride*. I'd be so busy I often got back to the depot 6 or 7 hours late!

SEXY

Sometimes I would do a country route just to give myself a rest. But on one occasion that plan back fired. I was driving to this village where no-one lived so I knew I'd have a quiet run. Little did I know a dozen top models had been posing for a sexy calendar in the countryside, and they all got on my bus to go home. I drove around the countryside for several hours, stopping on request to *punch their tickets*. When we eventually got back to the terminal I parked in a quiet corner and *got off* with all of them at once.

SEX

Mind you, its not all group sex on the buses. Sometimes I'd only have sex with one woman at a time. Like the time a gorgeous blond film star got on my bus. It was the last run of the evening and there was no-one else on board. She smiled and asked if I *went all the way*. I didn't need to be asked twice, and within seconds the windows were all steamed up and the suspension was being tested to its limit. By the time we'd finished – several hours later – the bus was a total write

off. I told the inspector I'd driven over some rough ground and he believed me. I still smile every time I drive past that old bus in the scrapyard.

HANDFUL

It wasn't always the passengers who provided the fun on the buses. The clippies were just as bad. I remember one in particular. Sandra was her name. On her first day the inspector asked me to *take her in hand*. And it wasn't long till I was showing her how to give someone *a fourpenny one*. With Sandra around there was always room for me *up top*. Quite a handful she was, I can tell you.

DOUBLE DECKER

Mind you, being a double decker romeo does have its hazards. I remember once I was having sex with this girl in my cab when her husband got on the bus! I've never put my regulation trousers on so quickly in my life! It was only when I got back to the depot that I realised I had them on back to front. My face was as red as my bus, I can tell you.

DOCTOR. I THINK I'M DEVELOPING SOMETHING

DARK ROOM

Another time I was stuck at some traffic lights so I decided to nip up top and have sex with a tasty housewife who'd given me the eye earlier. But while we were at it upstairs, a stern lady inspector boarded the bus. When she saw what was going on I thought I'd be sacked on the spot. But to my surprise she whipped off her tunic and joined in!

MILKY BAR

Our steamy sex session continued, even after the lights

had changed... again and again and again! There was quite a queue of cars behind the bus before those two ladies eventually *rang my bell* and I was able to move off. '

Next week: Les tells how his bus got stuck on a level crossing and it took eleven members of a passing Swedish hockey team to eventually *pull him off*.

Report slams police

The police yesterday.

A report published this month in the consumer watchdog magazine *What* reveals a majority of the British public believe the police force discriminates against minority groups.

OPINION

And it is the motorist who suffers most from police discrimination according to public opinion. Over 75% of the people questioned thought that police officers deliberately discriminated against drivers who drove either too fast, or in an erratic manner while under the influence of alcohol.

GROUPS

According to the survey other minority groups such as burglars are often singled out for attention by the police.

FEDERATION

A spokesman for the Federation of Policemen said that public confidence in Britain's

police was on the increase, despite the fact that they occassionally roughed people up or shot them by mistake. Meanwhile, a report published by the Police Complaints Commission, the Government's official independent police monitoring watchdog public accountability body, showed that the number of complaints made against police officers increased during the last year.

VAUX

A spokesman claimed that this was due to an increase in the number of complaints made over the past twelve months.

FREE!

Katie Boyle's EURO

Ever been embarrassed in a foreign country because you couldn't speak the language? I haven't, because I speak absolutely loads of languages, me, and now YOU can too with my FREE Eurovision Lingua-specs. Behind the 'polaroid' style fashion frames you can insert a wealth of euro-information and foreign phrases for your quick and easy reference. So no matter where you are abroad or what you want to say, just pop in the appropriate lingualens and "voilla" – you can speak foreign, just like me.

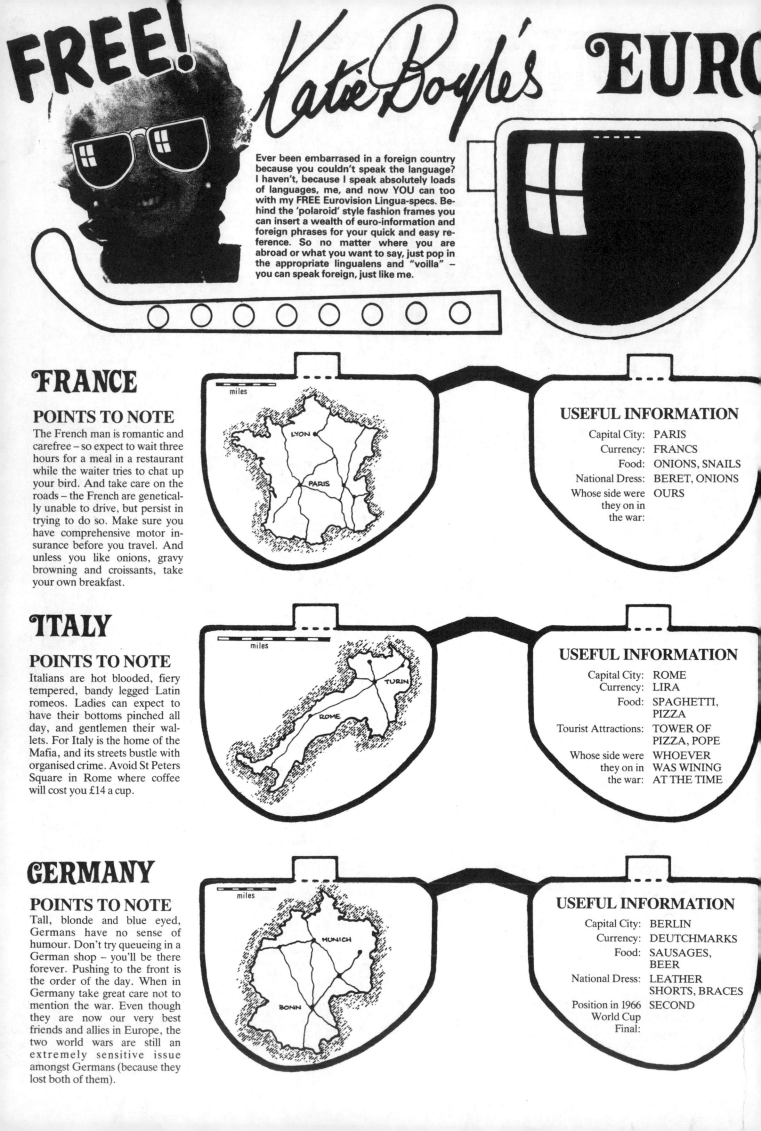

FRANCE

POINTS TO NOTE

The French man is romantic and carefree – so expect to wait three hours for a meal in a restaurant while the waiter tries to chat up your bird. And take care on the roads – the French are genetically unable to drive, but persist in trying to do so. Make sure you have comprehensive motor insurance before you travel. And unless you like onions, gravy browning and croissants, take your own breakfast.

miles

LYON
PARIS

USEFUL INFORMATION

Capital City: PARIS
Currency: FRANCS
Food: ONIONS, SNAILS
National Dress: BERET, ONIONS
Whose side were they on in the war: OURS

ITALY

POINTS TO NOTE

Italians are hot blooded, fiery tempered, bandy legged Latin romeos. Ladies can expect to have their bottoms pinched all day, and gentlemen their wallets. For Italy is the home of the Mafia, and its streets bustle with organised crime. Avoid St Peters Square in Rome where coffee will cost you £14 a cup.

miles

TURIN
ROME

USEFUL INFORMATION

Capital City: ROME
Currency: LIRA
Food: SPAGHETTI, PIZZA
Tourist Attractions: TOWER OF PIZZA, POPE
Whose side were they on in the war: WHOEVER WAS WINING AT THE TIME

GERMANY

POINTS TO NOTE

Tall, blonde and blue eyed, Germans have no sense of humour. Don't try queueing in a German shop – you'll be there forever. Pushing to the front is the order of the day. When in Germany take great care not to mention the war. Even though they are now our very best friends and allies in Europe, the two world wars are still an extremely sensitive issue amongst Germans (because they lost both of them).

miles

MUNICH
BONN

USEFUL INFORMATION

Capital City: BERLIN
Currency: DEUTCHMARKS
Food: SAUSAGES, BEER
National Dress: LEATHER SHORTS, BRACES
Position in 1966 World Cup Final: SECOND